Mathematics for
Elementary
School Teachers:
Explorations

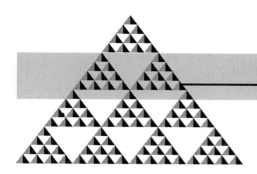

Mathematics for Elementary School Teachers: Explorations

Tom Bassarear
Keene State College

HOUGHTON MIFFLIN COMPANY   Boston   New York

Sponsoring Editor: *Maureen O'Connor*
Basic Book Editor: *Karla Paschkis*
Senior Project Editor: *Maria Morelli*
Associate Project Editor: *Tamela Ambush*
Senior Production/Design Coordinator: *Carol Merrigan*
Manufacturing Manager: *Florence Cadran*
Marketing Manager: *Charles Cavaliere*

Cover design: *Stoltze Design*
Photographer: *Y. Takahashi*, Photonica

PHOTO CREDITS
Chapter 9:
Page 242, © Breck P. Kent/EARTH SCENES

Printed in the U.S.A.

Library of Congress Catalog Card Number: 96-76861

ISBN: 0-395-66960-X

23456789-B-00   99   98   97

CONTENTS

4 *Number Theory*   79

5 *Extending the Number System*   97

6 *Proportional Reasoning*   137

7 *Uncertainty: Data and Chance*   149

10   *Geometry as Measurement*   259

PREFACE

Having a textbook contain two different volumes created a dilemma of where to put the Preface. We resolved this dilemma by having two prefaces. This one, to the Explorations, sets the overall theme of the course and explains how the two volumes work with each other. The Preface to the Text more specifically describes the goals of the course and the textbook features. For semantic reasons, this preface is addressed to the student and the Text Preface is addressed to the instructor. However, I have written each with the belief that student and instructor will find both prefaces useful.

I have been teaching the Mathematics for Elementary School Teachers course for 10 years, and in that time have learned as much from students like you as they have learned from me. The Explorations and the Text reflect the most important things we have taught each other: that building an understanding of mathematics is an active, exploratory process, and ultimately a rewarding, pleasurable one. Many students who have used draft versions of this text have said that it is the most readable and interesting mathematics textbook they have ever read. This is exciting to hear, because I thoroughly enjoy mathematics and hope others will too. At the same time, I know that far from loving mathematics, many people are actually afraid of it. If this book is successful, you will come to believe that math can be enjoyable and interesting (if you don't already feel that way), that mathematics is more than just numbers and formulas and is an important part of the curriculum, and that mathematical thinking can be done by "regular people."

What is it we want you to learn?

At its root, the purpose of this course is to revisit the content of K–8 mathematics so that you can build an integrated understanding of mathematical concepts and procedures. From one perspective, it is useful to talk about content knowledge (e.g., different meanings of subtraction, why we need a common denominator when adding fractions, and classification of geometric figures) and process knowledge (e.g., problem-solving and being able to communicate mathematical ideas and solutions). Let me give some examples of the kinds of content knowledge you can expect to learn in this book.

Content Knowledge   Virtually all adults can do the division problem at the right. If asked to describe the procedure, most descriptions would sound something like this: "4 'gazinta' (goes into) 9 two times, put the 2 above the 9, 4 times 2 is 8, 9 − 8 is 1, bring down the 2, 4 gazinta 12 three times with no remainder, put the 3 above the 2, the answer is 23." However, few adults can explain mathematically what "goes into" and "bring down" mean, other than by saying "that's how you do it." However, once you realize that one (of several) meanings of division is that an amount is to be distributed equally into groups and once you realize that 92 can be represented as 9 tens and 2 ones, then you can explain why long division works. Being able to explain *why* gives one what we call mathematical power, which means, among other things, that you can apply this knowledge to solve problems that are not just like the ones in the book. You can solve "real-life" problems, which is one of the most important goals of school mathematics.

Similarly, most elementary teachers recall that an approximation of π (pi) is 3.14 and they may remember some formulas: $C = \pi d$, $C = 2\pi r$, $A = \pi r^2$, but they can't explain what π means or why these formulas work. Developing a conceptual understanding of π is not as esoteric as many people think. Let me illustrate. Look at the circle at the right and answer the following question: Imagine we had several flexible rulers that were the same length as the diameter. If you wrapped those rulers around the circle, how many rulers would it take to wrap around the entire circle? If you actually do this, you find that it will take a little more than three rulers. Thus, one conception of π is that the length of the circumference of a circle is always a bit more than 3 times the length of the diameter. With this conceptual understanding, the formula C = πd "makes sense." Ensuring that math makes sense is another key goal of mathematics education.

I have just outlined two of many explorations and investigations that you will do over the course of this book. What so many of my students have discovered is that if they have a chance to work with mathematical concepts in an active, exploratory manner, they can make sense of elementary mathematics, which means that they will be much more effective teachers. Much of the impetus for teaching to foster this style of learning comes from the National Council of Teachers of Mathematics (NCTM), which has published three sets of Standards in the past decade and ushered in a new reform movement in mathematics education. I find that many students who enter the course with negative feelings toward mathematics view the NCTM Standards very positively. Many tell me, "I wish this is what my mathematics courses had been like."

NCTM   The first NCTM Standards document, *Curriculum and Evaluation Standards,* was published in 1989. It sets forth a vision of why mathematics is important for all citizens to know and describes the mathematical knowledge one should develop by the end of high school. Chapter 1 of the Text will explore the Curriculum Standards in more detail. The *Professional Standards for Teaching Mathematics* will be discussed later, and you should expect to examine the *Assessment Standards for School Mathematics* in your methods course. Since one of my goals is that you will use NCTM to frame your own teaching, I will discuss my vision of using NCTM Standards as much as possible. At appropriate times in the text, I will cite passages from the NCTM documents, and you can find the full Summaries of the Curriculum Standards in Appendix C at the back of the Text and Teaching Standards on the inside back cover of this textbook.

What does it mean to learn?

As you will discover in Chapter 1, your attitudes and beliefs have a lot to do with how you learn mathematics. My beliefs about what it means to "know" mathematics have led me to create a very different kind of textbook, and it is important for me to describe my sense of what it means to learn. Let me contrast some traditional beliefs about mathematical learning (which I disagree with) with this book's approach, then describe how this book is structured.

Active versus Passive Understanding   Many students believe that mathematical understanding is either-or; e.g., you either know fractions or you don't. In actuality, mathematical understanding is very much like other kinds of knowledge—you "sort of" know some things, you know other things "pretty well," and so on. The belief in either-or leads many students to focus on trying to get answers instead of trying to make sense of problems and situations. However, when learning is seen as an "it" that the students are supposed to "get," the student's role is seen more passively. Our language betrays this bias—the teacher "covers the material" and the students "absorb." Steven Leinwand, from the Connecticut State Department of Education, once told a joke at a mathematics teachers' convention about the Martian who came to visit

American schools. In her report to the Martians, she said, "Teachers are people who work really hard and students are people who watch teachers working really hard." In a similar vein, the NCTM has a button that reads: "Mathematics is not a spectator sport." Much of the joy of mathematics is observing a situation or problem and trying to understand it. My own experience with elementary school children and my two children, Emily and Josh, has convinced me that young children naturally seek to make sense of the world that they live in, and that for a variety of reasons many people slowly lose that curiosity over time.

Worthwhile Mathematical Tasks versus Oversimplified Problems   Another common belief about learning mathematics is that we should make the initial problems as simple and straightforward as possible. I call this approach the Lysol approach—we clean up the problems to reduce the complexity (we use routine problems and one-step problems), we try to make the problems unambiguous, and we get rid of extraneous information (we make sure to use everything in the problems). However, one of the biggest drawbacks of this approach is that most of the problems that people solve outside of classrooms are complex and ambiguous, and part of the problem is to determine what information is relevant. A famous Sufi story nicely illustrates the difference between the two approaches. Nasruddin came home one night and found a friend outside on his hands and knees looking in the dirt. When Nasruddin asked, "What's happening?" his friend replied, "I dropped my keys." Nasruddin asked, "Where did you drop them?" His friend pointed: "Over there." Puzzled, Nasruddin asked, "Then why are we looking here?" The response: "Oh, the light is much clearer here." Although the light is much clearer when the problems are unambiguous, routine, and one-step, that is just not how students learn to think mathematically. One consequence of these richer problems (NCTM uses the term "worthwhile mathematical tasks") is that most students report that the problems are much more interesting than what they generally find in texts.

Owning versus Renting   Another way of describing these two very different beliefs about learning mathematics that many of my students have found illuminating is to talk of the difference between owning and renting knowledge. Many students report that one year after finishing a mathematics course, they have forgotten most of what they learned—i.e., if they retook the final exam, they would fail. This means that they rented the knowledge they learned: they kept it long enough for the tests, and then it was gone. However, this need not be so. If you are an active participant in the learning process and if the instructional strategies of the professor fit with how you learn, then you will own most of what you learn. When you take your methods course in a year or so, you will still remember the important ideas from this course. It is such a wonderful feeling to know that you got more than just 3 or 4 credits for the 100+ hours you spent over the course of the semester. If you plan to be an excellent elementary teacher (and I expect you all do), then you need to own what you learn.

An Integrated Approach   If we want students to retain the knowledge, then how they learn it has to be different that it has been in traditional classrooms. One of my favorite words, and one you will find in the NCTM Standards, is *grapple*. I have found that if students grapple with problems and situations and try to make sense of them, they are more likely to retain what they learn in the process. I believe that a central part of the teacher's job is to select worthwhile tasks (Professional Standard 1) and to develop an environment that invites all students to learn and that honors differences in how they learn (Professional Standard 5). A classroom consistent with the NCTM vision does not look like a traditional classroom in which the teacher mostly lectures and demonstrates, and students generally take notes, ask questions, and answer questions the teacher asks. Rather, the classroom looks like an ongoing dialogue: the teacher presents a problem, possibly a brief lecture, and then the teacher facilitates the discussion around that question or situation (Professional Standards 2, 3, and 4), during which students naturally expect to make guesses (predictions and hypotheses) and try to explain their thinking and justify their hypotheses. Similarly, I believe that the textbook for this classroom must be different from a traditional book in which the important concepts and formulas are highlighted and in which the problems at the end of the chapter are generally pretty much like the examples.

In the Introduction to NCTM's *Professional Standards for Teaching Mathematics*, the authors summarize Major Shifts in mathematics classrooms that have been called for by the NCTM. This passage nicely summarizes much of what I have just described.

We need to shift:

- toward classrooms as mathematical communities—away from classrooms as simply collections of individuals;

- toward logic and mathematical evidence as verification—away from the teacher as the sole authority for right answers;

- toward mathematical reasoning—away from merely memorizing procedures;

- toward conjecturing, inventing, and problem-solving—away from an emphasis on mechanistic answer finding;

- toward connecting mathematics, its ideas, and its applications—away from treating mathematics as a body of isolated concepts and procedures.

If we can convince our students that fundamentally mathematics is a sense-making enterprise, then we change not only how much they work but also how they work. That is, if they see the relevance of the problems and concepts and develop confidence, they work harder; if they see the goal as sense making versus "getting it," they work differently. With this brief overview of what I mean by learning, let me explain how the two volumes work together.

Role of Explorations and Text

As just mentioned, if we believe that people learn better by grappling with richer problems (Worthwhile Mathematical Tasks) as opposed to being shown how to do simpler problems, then this creates a whole host of changes in what the classroom looks like, what the instructional materials look like, and how students' knowledge is assessed. Basically, these Explorations have been designed to have you grapple with important mathematical ideas. I have posed questions and tasks that call on you to discover fundamental mathematical concepts and structures, for example, that percents can be seen as proportions. In the Explorations, you grapple with new ideas and concepts in a hands-on environment. The Text then serves as a resource: a place where the formal definitions and structures are laid out (to be used generally after the Explorations), a place to refine your understanding, a place to self-assess (I can do this on my own and get immediate feedback), and of course, a source of homework problems. The Explorations in this volume are generally open-ended and often have more than one valid answer, whereas the Investigations (in the Text) are generally more focused in scope and, though they generally have one correct answer, the discussions following the Investigations show that they always lend themselves to different ways to arrive at that answer. I generally begin each new chapter with an Exploration that, in learning theory terms, enables/encourages/requires students to construct a scaffolding (i.e., focus on major structures). I then use the Text as a resource to see the concepts articulated in an organized way.

Looking back is a habit of mind that I want to encourage. A famous mathematics teacher proverb is "you're not finished when you have an answer; you're finished when you have an answer that makes sense to you." I model this notion explicitly in Chapter 1 in the Explorations and in the Text and you'll see it often in both volumes. The idea of reflection is new to many students, but getting into the habit of looking back is a great way to take ownership of this content. With this in mind, I hope you're looking forward to exploring elementary mathematics.

Mathematics for Elementary School Teachers: Explorations

1

Foundations for Learning Mathematics

You are about to begin what we hope is a very exciting course for you—a course in which you will come to appreciate the importance and relevance of elementary mathematical in our society, and a course in which you will come to a deeper understanding of the mathematical concepts behind the many mathematical procedures you know. For example, you will discover why we "move over" in the second row when multiplying large numbers, why we find a common denominator when adding fractions but not when multiplying fractions, what π means, and much more.

One of the major differences between this text and other mathematics texts arises from a growing belief that students learn mathematics best by using explorations to investigate and understand mathematical concepts, ideas, and procedures, rather than having the teacher explain to you the concepts, ideas, and procedures. Both volumes have been designed to present you with what the National Council of Teachers of Mathematics (NCTM) has called "worthwhile mathematical tasks."

There are many characteristics of worthwhile mathematical tasks upon which most teachers would be likely to agree. Let us discuss a few. A worthwhile task contains significant mathematics that will require the students to think (as opposed to memorize or follow a procedure). As a result of working on a worthwhile task, students should find that they have come to a deeper, richer understanding of a mathematical concept. Depending on the task, this might mean that they understand a mathematical concept more fully, that they understand why a mathematical procedure works, that they see connections that they hadn't seen before, or that they have added to their problem-solving repertoire, to name but a few possibilities. Two other characteristics of worthwhile mathematical tasks concern the students. First, to be worthwhile, the task must be interesting to the students. Second, the task should be rich enough so that all students can be both challenged by the task and yet be able to feel some success in the doing of the task. To the extent that a course is rich in worthwhile mathematical tasks, to that extent the students will come to feel more positive toward mathematics, they will acquire confidence in being able to do mathematics, and they will believe that mathematics can and does make sense to "regular" people.

To the extent that these explorations are successful, not only will you learn quite a bit of what is traditionally called mathematical content, but you will also develop more competence with respect to the abilities articulated in the first four Standards found in the *Curriculum and Evaluation Standards* published by the National Council of Teachers of Mathematics in 1989. That is:

- *Mathematics as problem solving*   You will become a more powerful and more confident problem solver.
- *Mathematics as communication*   You will appreciate the role of discussion in learning mathematics, and you will appreciate the value of vocabulary and notation as tools that make communication easier.
- *Mathematics as reasoning*   Your ability to use reasoning—deductive, inductive, and intuitive—will grow, and you will be able to justify your hypotheses and solutions.
- *Mathematical connections*   You will be more aware of connections between various mathematical topics and connections between mathematics and other areas.

As you do these explorations, please keep the NCTM Standards in mind, especially the four standards just mentioned, and use the "4 Steps for Solving Problems" guidelines to help you when you become stuck. When you take your Methods course later in your studies, you will then examine how to develop lessons that are consistent with the NCTM Standards. To the extent that you consider the Standards as a *learner* of mathematics, to that extent you will be able to use the Standards more skillfully as a *teacher* of mathematics. At the end of each exploration, you will be asked to "look back"; this activity will help you to reflect on what you have learned.

EXPLORATION 1.1   **The Handshakes Problem**

More and more teachers are having students solve problems in small groups. This method of instruction, called cooperative learning, works better if the students know one another by name.

Determine how many students are in your class, including yourself. The question we will investigate is: If each student shakes hands with every other student in the class, how many handshakes will there be?

1.   Write your ideas about how you might solve this problem. Can you apply ideas discussed in the preface to find patterns in this problem? Can you use what you see to help you plan a solution?

2.   Discuss your ideas in your small group or the whole class, as your teacher directs. Write down new ideas that you like.

3. Now solve the problem. Keep in mind the "4 Steps for Solving Problems" guidelines from the inside cover of this text and refer to them as needed by asking yourself the following questions: Do you understand the problem? Do you have a plan? Are you monitoring your work? Did you check your solution?

4. After the class discussion of the problem, select a solution path that was different from the one you used. Explain that way of doing the problem, as if you were speaking to a student who was not in class today.

EXPLORATION 1.2   **Who Owes Whom How Much?**

The Neighbor Problem

This exploration begins with a real-life problem. When I was writing this book, my four-year-old son and our next-door neighbor's four-year-old son went to the same babysitter. At Christmas, the families wanted to do something nice together for the babysitter. My wife bought a gift certificate for $30 for the babysitter and her husband at a local restaurant. Our next-door neighbor bought gifts for both of the babysitter's children; she spent $18 for the gifts. My wife came to me and asked how much our next-door neighbor owed us.

1. Take a few minutes to work on this problem alone. Be prepared to explain your thinking.

2. Compare your answer and your solution path (that is, *how* you solved the problem) with others in your group or others in your class.

The Conference Problem

Now let us make the problem a bit more complex. Sally loaned Leah $10. Leah bought a book for Sally at a conference; the book cost $24. The two went out to dinner. They agreed to split the bill, which came to $40. They found out after the meal that the restaurant didn't accept credit cards. Looking through her wallet, Sally discovered that she only had $11. Leah barely had enough in her wallet, but they made the $40. Who owes whom how much?

3. Take a few minutes to work on this problem alone. Are you inclined to use the same method to solve this problem that you used for the neighbor problem, or are you inclined to use or adapt a method that you heard another student describe? Solve the problem, showing your work.

4. Compare your results with those of other students in your group or your class.

5. If you are satisfied with your answer and your solution path, move on. If you are dissatisfied with either your answer (you now think it's wrong) or your solution

path (you find that someone else's method makes more sense or is simpler), do the problem again.

a. If your answer was wrong, describe the source of the error. Describe what problem-solving tools (such as checking your work, asking if what you are writing makes sense, being more systematic, etc.) could have helped you to find your error yourself.

b. If your answer was right, but you like another student's method, explain why that method works. *Note:* This is not the same as showing **what** you did, but rather explaining **why** what you did is correct. It often helps to imagine that you are having to explain the problem to someone who has no idea how to get the answer.

6. Make up a similar problem and solve it.

EXPLORATION 1.3   **Budgeting Expenses**

PART 1: How much will you spend on gasoline this year?

A problem most people face every day is figuring out whether they can afford something. Imagine that you are thinking of buying a car. Select one person in your group who has a car and use data about that person's car to determine how much that person will spend on gasoline in one year.

1.   a. Brainstorm the information you need to have in order to answer this question.

b. Select the information that you all agree needs to be collected and briefly explain why each piece of information is necessary to answer the question.

c. Decide how you can get that information. Briefly explain the reasoning behind each decision.

d. Decide how accurate your information needs to be. That is, if the actual amount were $10 different from your estimate, would that be accurate enough? What if it were $100 different? Briefly explain your reasoning.

2. Using the data that you have at your disposal, determine how much the person should budget for gasoline per month. Prepare a presentation of your solution that includes your work on Steps 1(b)–1(d).

3.   Listen to other groups' presentations.

   a.   What assumptions did other groups make that were similar to your group's assumptions?

   b.   What assumptions did they make that were different?

   c.   How did different assumptions affect the answers that groups came up with?

PART 2: How much does it cost to own a car?

As in Part 1, select one person's car and personal data to determine how much it costs that person to own a car for a year. If no one in your group has a car, select one person to "buy" a car, and then determine how much it would cost, per year, for that person to own the car.

1.   **a.**   Brainstorm the information you need to have in order to answer this question.

   b.   Select the information that you all agree needs to be collected and briefly explain why each piece of information is necessary to answer the question.

   c.   Decide how you can get that information. Briefly explain the reasoning behind each decision.

   d.   Decide how accurate your information needs to be. That is, if the actual amount were $10 different from your estimate, would that be accurate enough? What if it were $100 different? Briefly explain your reasoning.

2.   Using the data that you have at your disposal, determine how much it costs that person to own a car for a year. Prepare a presentation of your solution that includes your work on Steps 1(b)–1(d).

3.   Listen to other groups' presentations.

   a.   What assumptions did other groups make that were similar to your group's assumptions?

   b.   What assumptions did they make that were different?

    c. How did different assumptions affect the answers that groups came up with?

EXPLORATION 1.4   **How Many Squares?**

The following exploration comes from a question a child asked his parent while playing checkers: How many squares of any size are in the checkerboard?

1.   **a.** Before you actually begin to determine the answer, first stop to think about how you might go about solving the problem. Write your thoughts.

    b. Share your ideas with other members of your group. Briefly describe what you learned from the discussion. For example, did you get ideas about how to use your strategy more effectively; did you hear of a new strategy that you like better?

    c. Now solve the problem in your own way.

    d. Listen to how other students solved the problem. Note any ideas that you heard that you would like to remember, such as specific strategies for solving this problem or tools that might help in other kinds of problems too.

2.   How many rectangles of any size are in the figure at the right?

    a. Discuss your interpretations of this question with other members of your group. That is, what does the question mean? Write your present interpretation.

    b. Solve the problem in your own way. Can you apply strategies you learned when determining the number of squares, or do you have to develop new strategies?

    c. Listen to how other students solved the problem. Note any ideas that you heard that you would like to remember, such as specific strategies for solving this problem or tools that might help in other kinds of problems too.

EXPLORATION 1.5   **Magic Squares**

Have you ever seen a magic square? Magic squares have fascinated human beings for many thousands of years. The oldest recorded magic square, the Lo Shu magic square shown in the figure below, dates to 2200 B.C. It is supposed to have been marked on the back of a divine tortoise that appeared before Emperor Yu when he was standing on the bank of the Yellow River.

The Lo Shu magic square

In the Middle Ages, many people considered magic squares to be able to protect them against illness! Even in the twentieth century, people in many countries still use magic squares as amulets.

We will spend some time exploring magic squares because they reveal some amazing patterns. As a teacher, you will find that many of your students love working with magic squares and other magic figures.

PART 1: Describing magic squares and finding patterns

1. Let us begin with the simple magic square shown in the figure. Take a couple of minutes to write down why this is a magic square and to write down all the patterns you see in this square.

8	1	6
3	5	7
4	9	2

2. Compare your observations with those of others in your group. Add to your list new observations and patterns that you heard from other members.

3. Take a few minutes to think of questions you might have about magic squares. Write down these questions.

4. Listen to the questions from other students. Your instructor may select additional questions to investigate.

5. Based on your observations and discussion, what makes a magic square "magic"? Imagine telling this to a friend in another state who has never heard of magic squares.

PART 2: Patterns in all 3 × 3 magic squares

1. Make a completely new 3 × 3 magic square. You are not restricted to consecutive numbers, though I suggest restricting yourself to positive whole numbers, simply to make it easier to see patterns that are true in all the magic squares.

2. Display each magic square. Have each person explain any strategies that made the creation of the square easier, that is, strategies beyond "grope and hope." Note any strategies that you did not discover but that you would like to remember.

3. Allow some individual time for each person to note patterns that seem to occur in *every* magic square and patterns that occur only in *some* magic squares. Then go around the group and have members share their responses.

   a. Record patterns that seem to be true for all magic squares.

   b. Record patterns that seem to be true for some magic squares but not for others.

4. Reflect on the patterns that are true for all 3 × 3 magic squares and reflect on the strategies that students found to make a magic square. Imagine that you are talking on the phone to a friend about your discoveries, and that your friend is skeptical that you can make a magic square with brand new numbers.

   a. Using everyday English, describe how to make a generic 3 × 3 magic square.

   b. Give these directions to someone who is not in this course and have that person make a new magic square, using only your directions. If the person had any difficulties with your directions, write an explanation of the difficulty and of how you would modify the directions to reduce the possibility that a new person would have that difficulty. If the person was not able to make the magic square from your directions, discuss the difficulties with the person, then write a new set of directions and repeat this step.

PART 3: Using algebra to describe 3 × 3 magic squares

1. As you may have already discovered, the middle number of the 3 × 3 magic square is a key number. What if we called the middle number m? Reflect on the patterns you observed in all magic squares and the strategies students used to construct magic squares. Can we represent the other numbers in the magic square in terms of m? With the group working together, take a few minutes to think about this question, look at relationships between the middle number and other

numbers in the sequence. Describe your present thinking and work before moving on.

2.   One key to solving this problem is to realize how many more variables are needed. The only algebraic representation of 3×3 magic squares that I know of requires two more variables. Let us call them x and y. In other words, by using m, x, and y, we can represent the value of each cell in the magic square. Work on this problem in your group and then draw your magic square. Briefly explain, in writing, how you solved the problem.

3.   At this point, you have a solution, generated either from your group or from the whole class discussion. Think about your description of how to make a generic magic square in Part 2, Step 4, and then read the following quote. Does this experience change your attitude toward algebra? Does it help you to see the use of symbols in a new light? Briefly explain your response.

Mathematics is often considered a difficult and mysterious science, because of the numerous symbols which it employs. . . .[T]he technical terms of any profession or trade are incomprehensible to those who have never been trained to use them. But this is not because they are difficult in themselves. On the contrary they have invariably been introduced to make things easy. So in mathematics, granted that we are giving any serious attention to mathematical ideas, the symbolism is invariably an immense simplification.[1]

PART 4: Further explorations

1.   How many different magic squares can you make starting with the two numbers shown in the figure?

3		
		7

2.   Below are questions about four possible transformations of a 3×3 magic square. In each case, write your initial guess and your reasoning before you test your guess. Then test your guess. If you were correct, refine your justification if needed. If you were wrong, look for a flaw or incompleteness in your reasoning. If you were wrong, can you now justify the correct answer?

    a.   If you doubled each number in a magic square, would it still be a magic square?

    b.   If you added the same number to each number in a magic square, would it still be a magic square?

[1] Alfred North Whitehead, *Introduction to Mathematics*, New York, 1911, pp. 59–69, cited in Robert Moritz, *On Mathematics* (New York: Dover Publications, 1914), p. 199.

    c. If you multiplied each number in the magic square by 3 and then subtracted 2 from that number, would you still have a magic square?

    d. If you squared each number in the magic square, would it still be a magic square?

3. Look back on your data from different magic squares, and answer the following questions:

    a. Is there a relationship between the magic sum and whether the number in the center is even or odd?

    b. Divide the set of magic squares into two subsets: those in which the nine numbers are consecutive numbers (for example, 10–18) and those in which the nine numbers are not consecutive numbers. Are there any other differences between these two sets of magic squares?

Looking Back

1. You have done several explorations during the course of this first chapter. Take a few minutes to think back on those explorations. What did you learn? Jot down your thoughts before reading on.

    Now let us take some time to reflect on some specific things you have learned in this chapter.

2. Select the one problem-solving tool on which you feel you have made the most progress during this chapter. You may pick one from the "4 Steps for Solving Problems" guidelines, or you may describe a tool you used that is not on that list.

    a. Give the tool a name. If it is a tool mentioned in the book, you can use that name, but you are encouraged to develop names that describe your own perspective.

    b. Show *how* you used that tool to solve a problem. Imagine describing this tool to a reader who does not yet have this tool in the repertoire. How can you help that reader to see not just *what* you did but also *how* this tool helped you to solve the problem so that the reader can get a sense of how this tool works?

3. Many students enter this course not knowing how to check their answers, other than by checking their computation. What have you learned about being able to "verify and interpret results with respect to the original problem" (*Curriculum Standards*, p. 23) in the course of these explorations?

4. In what ways have these explorations helped you to feel more "confidence in using mathematics meaningfully" (*Curriculum Standards*, p. 23)?

5. We want students to be able to "justify their answers and solution processes" (*Curriculum Standards*, p. 29). Again, this idea is new for many students. In what ways has having to justify your answers and solution processes — to the instructor on an assignment, to a group member in a discussion, and to yourself while working on a problem — helped make you a stronger learner of mathematics?

6. Although the use of patterns is included as one of the major problem-solving tools, it also appears in Standard 3 (Mathematics as Reasoning): We want students to be able to "use patterns and relationships to analyze mathematical situations" (*Curriculum Standards*, p. 29). In what ways have these explorations helped you to *see* patterns better? For example, did you find that seeing and then analyzing a pattern (by using reasoning, tables, etc.) was a key to solving one of the problems?

Fundamental Concepts

The concepts of sets, functions, and numeration permeate elementary mathematics. The goals of the explorations in this chapter are for you to recognize and be comfortable with these fundamental concepts. Throughout the book, we will run into situations in which set and function ideas enable us to communicate more easily and will help us to understand and solve problems. Similarly, a deeper understanding of numeration systems will enable you to develop what NCTM calls mathematical power.

SECTION 2.1 **EXPLORING SETS**

As you will discover in your course on mathematical methods, the concept of sets (and subsets) is an important aspect of the development of logical thinking in young children.

Do you know that Jean Piaget, a Swiss psychologist, used set concepts to help determine the extent to which a young child could reason abstractly? He learned how children's thinking developed by conducting "interviews" with children, one of which is illustrated below. A child is given a set of objects that are all mixed together. The child is then asked to separate the objects into two or three groups so that "each group is alike in some way." Do this yourself and record your different answers.

Children who have moved from what we call preoperational thinking to concrete operational thinking are able, fairly quickly and easily, to make subsets like the following: triangles, circles, and squares; big shapes and small shapes; white shapes and black shapes. Children who are still preoperational are not able to make these classifications as easily and consistently. It is not easy for them to hold the three attributes (color, shape, and size) of each object simultaneously in their minds. The following explorations are designed to enhance your ability to work with sets and subsets so that when you work with children, you will be able to recognize and nurture this important aspect of children's "mathematical" thinking.

EXPLORATION 2.1 **Gathering and Interpreting Data**

This exploration involves collecting data and then using set ideas to analyze that data.

Many writers have described our era as the Computer Age. Many items that are found in most homes today either did not exist 20 years ago or were found in only a small percentage of homes. Think of the household you belong to; if you live in a dormitory, think of your parents' home or your previous home. Does that household have a computer, an answering machine, or a compact disc player?

1. *Ask the questions*   If we consider the students in this class as a subset of the set of college students, what questions might you ask concerning ownership of these items?

   a. Write the questions that you would like to ask, then discuss the questions.

   b. After the class discussion, write the questions that will actually be asked.

2. *Gather the data*   Determine how you will gather the data in order to answer the questions you are asking.

   a. Write your proposed method.

   b. After the class discussion, write the method that will be used. If this method is different from the one in part (a), discuss and then describe the advantages of the method that the whole class chose over the method that you described in (a).

3. *Answer the questions*

   a. In your group, discuss how you can represent the information that you gathered in order to answer the questions.

   b. Prepare a brief report that includes your answers to the questions, a description of how you determined the answers, and your representation of the information (a chart or diagram).

EXPLORATION 2.2 **Understanding Venn Diagrams**

In this exploration, we will explore Venn diagrams as a tool for gathering and reporting data about different subsets of a set.

Consider the following Venn diagram, in which the areas listed below represent various sets of students:

- *U* represents the set of students in this class.
- *D* represents the set of students who have at least one dog.
- *C* represents the set of students who have at least one cat.
- *R* represents the set of students who have at least one rodent, such as a rat, mouse, gerbil, hamster, or guinea pig.

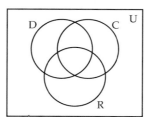

1. Write your initials in the region in which your household belongs. If you live in a dormitory, think of your parents' home or your previous home. Then discuss the diagram with other members of your group. Each member should show where his or her name was placed and why.

In Steps 2 through 5, refer to the class Venn diagram on an overhead projector or blackboard.

2. Which subset has more members: students who have cats and dogs, students who have cats and rodents, or students who have dogs and rodents? How did you figure this out?

3. What fraction (percentage) of the class has at least one dog?

4. How would you describe in words the subset of the class whose names are outside all three circles?

5. Describe a different subset of the class:

a. In words

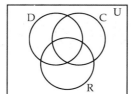

b. With a Venn diagram

6. How would you describe the subset of the class that has no pets?

a. Write down your thoughts about this question.

b. Discuss the question in your group or with the whole class. If you change your mind as a result of the discussion, describe your new thoughts and also describe why you changed your mind.

EXPLORATION 2.3   **Analyzing Different Representations**

Let's say you were going to gather information about the relative popularity of various recreational activities. For example, in the past month, how many students at your college have gone to a movie, a sporting event, or a cultural event?

1.   Decide on the number of categories and the description of each category. Then write down the questions that you want to be able to answer after collecting the information.

2.   Assume that someone has collected information that will enable you to answer your questions. Discuss the various ways in which you could represent this information. Summarize the advantages and disadvantages or limitations of each kind of representation.

Representation	Advantages	Disadvantages/limitations

EXPLORATION 2.4   **Blood Types**

Have you ever given blood? Do you know your blood type? Are you aware that people with certain blood types can receive only certain types of blood?

Blood type is determined in the following manner. If antigen A or B is present, that letter occurs in your blood type; that is, you are A, B, or AB. If you have neither the A nor the B antigen, your blood type is O. If you have the Rh antigen, a plus (+) follows the letter; if you do not have the Rh antigen, a minus (−) follows the letter.

1. How many different blood types do you think there are? Work on this yourself. Summarize your answer and briefly describe your thinking. For example, if you think there are six blood types, what are they and why do you think there are six?

2. Discuss your answers and your methods of representation with other members of your group. If you have different answers, discuss your ideas until you all agree on one answer.

    a. If your answer is different from that in Step 1, indicate your new answer and briefly justify this answer.

    b. If members of the group have different methods of representation (e.g., diagrams, tables), discuss them. Do some methods have advantages, or are they "all fine, with differences simply the result of personal preference"?

3. Your instructor will give you the percentages of each blood type. Make a diagram to display the data. Revisit the discussion about the advantages of different methods of representation. Describe any new observations.

4. Select two different ways of representing the different blood types. Describe the advantages and the disadvantages or limitations of the two representations.

Representation	Advantages	Disadvantages/limitations

5. Explain each representation so that the reader knows not only how many blood types there are but also how to interpret each representation.

Looking Back

1. You have done several explorations with sets. Take a few minutes to think back on those explorations. Select an important learning and describe that learning so that the reader gets a sense of what you learned, where and/or how that learning developed, and why it feels important.

2. Describe a situation that knowledge acquired in these Explorations would help you to analyze.

3. Describe something that you are still not clear about.

SECTION   2.2   **EXPLORING FUNCTIONS**

The concept of functions is one of the "big ideas" of mathematics. Although formal presentation of functions and other algebraic ideas does not happen until grade 8 or 9 in most schools, the foundation for understanding algebraic ideas is laid in elementary school. An essential component of this work has to do with patterns. We see patterns almost everywhere, both in everyday life and in work situations, and children love playing with patterns. We connect this natural fascination with patterns to mathematical thinking by focusing on recognizing, describing, and extending patterns. In this way, children "develop the ability to classify and organize information" (*Curriculum Standards,* p. 60).

> From the earliest grades, the curriculum should give students opportunities to focus on regularities in events, shapes, designs, and sets of numbers. Children should begin to see that regularity is the essence of mathematics. The idea of a functional relationship can be intuitively developed through observations of regularity and work with generalizable patterns.
>
> (*Curriculum Standards,* p. 60).

The notion of analyzing patterns and functional relationships has many real-life applications. One of the most poignant has to do with finding missing children. In one case, researchers helped investigators find two children who had been abducted by their father and had not been seen in eight years. Scott Barrows and Lewis Sadler developed a computer program that enabled them to take photographs of the five- and seven-year-old girls and create pictures of what they should look like eight years later. "The pictures showed up on TV one night and within 10 minutes a national hot line was getting calls from neighbors . . . by 7:30 the next morning the girls were in police custody."[1]

How had the researchers been able to do this? It seems that facial bones change in predictable ways throughout childhood. The two researchers determined relationships for 39 facial dimensions. By recognizing and analyzing the most important patterns, they were able to quite accurately predict what the girls would look like eight years

[1] *Newsweek,* Feb. 13, 1989, p. 62.

later. In the explorations and investigations in this chapter, you will explore patterns and see how the concept of functions connects to understanding patterns.

EXPLORATION 2.5   **Figurate Numbers**

Humans have long been fascinated by number patterns. The ancient Greeks thought of numbers as quantities made up of units, which they often expressed as dots.

Therefore, it was natural for them to "see" numbers—and number patterns—geometrically. Thus, they spoke of triangular numbers, square numbers, and so on. The first few square numbers and triangular numbers are shown below.

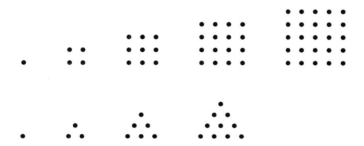

Exploration of these kinds of numbers, called **figurate numbers,** is done in many elementary schools. One reason is that it is developmentally appropriate for children, who generally need more concrete representations of mathematical ideas. Another reason is that there are many opportunities for doing good mathematics with these numbers—looking for patterns, making and testing predictions, learning how to develop formulas from patterns (remember Gauss's formula from Investigation 1.5: The Sum of the First 100 Numbers?).

Square Numbers

1. Let us look first at the set of square numbers. The first five square numbers are shown above.

    a. How many dots does the sixth square number contain?

    b. How many dots does the tenth square number contain?

    c. How many dots does the nth square number contain?

Triangular Numbers

Most students find it relatively easy to answer the three questions above, because the pattern is relatively simple. Let us now explore the set of triangular numbers. The Greeks saw the set of triangular numbers as literally *emerging* from the counting numbers. That is, they created them in the following manner: put one dot on top of two dots; this makes a triangle. Now put this triangle on top of three dots; this makes a new triangle. Continue in this manner. Since the stacks (except for the first one) look like triangles, the Greeks called this set of numbers triangular numbers. Note that the Greeks called 1 the first triangular number.

2.   **a.**   How many dots does the fifth triangular number contain? Write *how* you determined this amount.

   b.   How many dots does the sixth triangular number contain? Write *how* you determined this amount.

   c.   What patterns do you see that would enable you to predict the number of dots in the next triangular number? Write down the patterns you see and then compare your observations with others in your group. Add to your list useful patterns that others observed.

3.   **a.**   Now we will jump to what is called the general case: How many dots does the *n*th triangular number contain? Take a few minutes to explore this question on your own. Show your thinking. If you are stuck, consult the "4 Steps for Solving Problems" guidelines.

   b.   Compare your ideas with other members of your group. Add any new ideas to your list.

   c.   After the discussion, state the value of the *n*th triangular number and explain how you arrived at that value. If you are not sure, summarize your current thinking and where you are stuck.

   Once we have a way of describing the *n*th triangular number, we have uncovered the functional relationship. That is, we can now pick any triangular number and tell how many dots that triangular number contains, whether it is the 10th or the 250th triangular number. This leads into the next part of the exploration: how to communicate our discoveries and observations.

Interpreting a New Notation

There are many ways to look at the relationship between square numbers and triangular numbers and many ways to describe what we see.

4. The following formula expresses *one* way in which the two sets of numbers are related:

$$S_n = T_{n-1} + T_n$$

   a. Translate this equation to English.

   b. Exchange your translation with a partner and examine carefully your partner's translation with respect to accuracy and clarity. Discuss each of your translations until you both feel you understand the formula and can describe the formula in words.

   c. Work with your partner to justify this relationship, that is, to explain why it is true. Write your first draft of a justification.

Translating Words into Notation

5. The following sentence describes, in words, another way in which two sets of numbers are related: The square of any odd number is one more than eight times a specific triangular number. First, make sure you understand this statement.

   a. Translate this sentence into notation.

   b. Exchange your notation with a partner and critique your partner's notation with respect to accuracy and clarity.

Other Figurate Numbers

6. Look at the pentagonal numbers below.

   a. Describe patterns that you observe. You may want to draw the next few pentagonal numbers.

   b. Write questions or hypotheses about the pentagonal numbers and their relationship to triangular and square numbers.

7. Look at the hexagonal numbers below.

    a. Describe patterns that you observe. You may want to draw the next few hexagonal numbers.

    b. Write questions or hypotheses about the hexagonal numbers and their relationship to triangular and square numbers.

8. Write in your expressions for the value of the *n*th triangular number and the *n*th square number. Determine the value of the *n*th pentagonal number and the *n*th hexagonal number. Show your work.

Type of number	Value of the *n*th term
Triangular	
Square	
Pentagonal	
Hexagonal	

9. Certain relationships among different figurate numbers enable us to predict the value of the *n*th number for *any* figurate number family, such as the *n*th octagonal number. Describe at least one relationship among the formulas in Step 8 that would enable you to make such a prediction. Explain.

Non-Standard Figurate Numbers

Many, many kinds of figurate numbers have been created by mathematicians and nonmathematicians alike. For example, consider the L numbers below.

10. a. Describe the set of L numbers in words.

b. Describe the set of L numbers in relation to one or more of the other sets of figurate numbers.

c. Predict the 10th L number.

d. Predict the nth L number.

11. Make up another set of figurate numbers and describe what you can about that set.

Looking Back on Exploration 2.5

Describe one way in which your ability to recognize and extend patterns increased as a result of this exploration.

EXPLORATION 2.6 **Another Pattern**

Pattern blocks can be found in most elementary classrooms. They are one of the most versatile of the mathematics manipulatives because they can be used to explore mathematical concepts from functions to fractions to geometry to measurement.

A common pattern that has applications in many fields is what we call a growth pattern. Biologists are interested in understanding how fast bacteria or animals or plants are increasing. Epidemiologists want to know how fast an epidemic spreads. Businesspeople want to know how fast their company is growing. Employees want to know how fast their retirement fund is growing. We will use pattern blocks to model a simple growth situation. Note that I am using the word *simple* here to mean "not complex," as opposed to "not difficult."

1. Take a few minutes to play with the pattern blocks. Note your observations and then share these observations with other members of your group.

Building a Pattern Block Patio

Let's say that an eccentric couple has decided to make a huge patio in their back yard with concrete blocks that are in the shape of giant pattern blocks. The pattern they want to create will consist of rings of hexagons. That is, they begin with a hexagon and then make bigger and bigger rings around this hexagon. The diagram at the left shows the initial block, and the diagram at the

First ring   Second ring

right shows the first ring. If the hexagon costs $6 and the other blocks are valued proportionately, by surface area, then the initial block costs $6 and the first ring costs $18.

The ultimate question is: How much will the nth ring cost? That is, can you find patterns in this growth so that if the couple were to ask how much the 10th ring would cost, you could tell them without having to make a physical model of the whole design? What about the 15th ring? the 20th ring? The patterns and the ability to make predictions from the observed patterns will emerge if you begin with the initial block and then build from there.

2. **a.** Build the second and third rings and determine their respective costs.

     b. What patterns do you notice—either patterns that enable you to make the third ring or patterns in the numbers for the cost of the first, second, and third rings? Write down your observations.

     c. Do you see any patterns that might enable you to predict the cost of the fourth ring? If possible, make a hypothesis before you build the fourth ring.

3. **a.** Build the fourth ring and determine its cost.

     b. What patterns do you notice—either patterns that enable you to make the fourth ring or patterns in the numbers for the cost of each of the rings? Write down your observations.

     c. Do you see any patterns that might enable you to predict the cost of the fifth ring? If possible, make a hypothesis before you build the fifth ring.

4. **a.** Build the fifth ring and determine its cost.

     b. What patterns do you notice—either patterns that enable you to make the fifth ring or patterns in the numbers for the cost of each of the rings? Write down your observations.

     c. Do you see any patterns that might enable you to predict the cost of the sixth ring?

5. How much does the nth ring cost? If you have difficulty with this question, and many students do, the following ideas are often helpful.

- Fill in the Cost column of the following table.
- Think back to Chapter 1 when we expanded our tables in Investigation 1.1 (Pigs and Chickens) and in Investigation 1.5 (The Sum of the First 100 Numbers). Would an additional column help you to predict the cost of the nth ring?

Ring	Cost	
1		
2		
3		
4		
5		
6		
n		

6. Prepare a brief presentation of your group's work. One member of your group will present your answer to the question and explain how your group arrived at this answer.

7. What did you learn from hearing other groups' presentations and the ensuing class discussion?

Looking Back on Exploration 2.6

Describe one way in which your ability to recognize and extend patterns increased as a result of this exploration.

EXPLORATION 2.7 **Pendulum**

The development of more and more accurate ways to keep track of time has a fascinating history. Thousands of years ago, people developed water clocks, sandglasses, and sundials, but each of these had limitations. At some point in time, someone, somewhere realized that there was a functional relationship between the length of a pendulum and the time it took the pendulum to swing back and forth (called the *period* of the pendulum). However, it was not until the seventeenth century that the pendulum clock was perfected. Thus, the antique grandfather clock actually represents a rather great scientific advance, for the pendulum inside the clock enabled people to keep track of time more accurately than they had in the past.

PART 1: Initial explorations

1. What questions—both "mathematical" and "nonmathematical"—do you have about pendula (plural of pendulum)?

2.   **a.**   What variables do you think will affect the length of time it takes the pendulum to go back and forth once? This length of time is the pendulum's period.

  b.   Select one variable that you think might affect the pendulum's period and briefly describe how you would gather data to determine how that variable affects the period of the pendulum.

3.   Describe your exploration:

  a.   What did you do?

  b.   What data did you collect?

  c.   What conclusions can you make? How confident are you about your conclusions?

  d.   What other observations from the exploration seem worth sharing?

  e.   If you encountered and overcame difficulties or obstacles, describe one of them and how you overcame it.

4.   We will examine the relationship between one variable (length of the pendulum) and the period. However, before we can do that, we will have to determine how long a pendulum is. For example, look at the figure below, which shows a ring tied onto a string.
    Is the length of the pendulum the distance from the end of the string to the top of the ring, the distance from the end of the string to the bottom of the ring, or something else?

  a.   What distance do you choose as the length of the pendulum? Why?

  b.   Describe how we might find out which of these distances is the actual length of the pendulum.

  c.   Now do the experiment. First, describe what you did to answer the question. Then state and justify your conclusion.

PART 2: Predicting the period from the length

There are many questions we can answer concerning the relationship between the length and the period of a pendulum. In this part of the exploration, we will gather data on the periods of pendula of various lengths and then use our data to predict the period of a pendulum given its length.

1. a. First, take a minute to think about how you might determine the period. Note down your thoughts and discuss your ideas with other members of your group.

    b. Determine the periods of a pendulum 40 cm in length and 50 cm in length.

    c. Compare data and methods with other groups. Then note down the method the class has decided to use and briefly explain the reasoning behind the choice of this method.

2. a. Gather the data below.

Length of string	Period of your pendulum	Other groups' periods	Class period
40 cm			
50 cm			
60 cm			
70 cm			
80 cm			
90 cm			

    b. Compare your group's data with other groups' data and add their data to your table.

    c. Since there are differences among the groups' numbers, describe your thoughts about how to resolve these differences. That is, what is your proposal to determine the period you will use for each length; that is, the number in the last column? Briefly justify your proposal.

    d. After the class discussion, write and briefly explain the class's choice.

    e. Note the class period for each length.

3. **a.** Now use these data to predict the period of a 1-meter pendulum. Explain how you arrived at your prediction.

   b. Now determine the period of a 1-meter pendulum. What is the class result?

   c. How close was your prediction? Why do you think some groups were closer than others?

4. **a.** Use these data to predict the period of a 2-meter pendulum. Explain how you arrived at your prediction.

   Most students report that they are less confident of their prediction for a 2-meter pendulum than they were for a 1-meter pendulum. The jump from 1 meter to 2 meters is too big to make an accurate prediction. This example illustrates a difference between empirical research and theoretical research. The data from 40 centimeters, 50 centimeters, etc., were sufficient for predicting the period of a 1-meter pendulum, but such empirical data are not as useful for the 2-meter question. Several hundred years ago, scientists were able to combine their data and their growing knowledge about physics to discover the following relationship between the length of a pendulum and its period.
   The actual formula is

$$P = 2\pi \sqrt{\frac{L}{g}}$$

   where P is the period (in seconds), L is the length (in centimeters), and g is the acceleration due to gravity (980 cm/sec²).

   b. Predict the period of a 2-meter pendulum using this formula and then compare your first prediction with the prediction from the formula.

   c. Determine the period of a 2-meter pendulum. Note your result, and then determine the class result.

   d. How close is the class result to the number predicted by the formula?

   In Chapter 10 you will further investigate the topic of measurement. At this point, it is interesting to note that in 1790, Thomas Jefferson made a sweeping series of proposals to standardize the various systems of measurement then in use. Specifically, he proposed to have a pendulum of length x represent 1 second, so that 1 second would be the same throughout the United States.

5. Determine the length of a pendulum that would have a period of 1 second.

6. Show that the physics formula is approximately equivalent to $P = 0.2\sqrt{L}$.

Looking Back on Exploration 2.7

1. Describe something that you learned from this exploration.

2. Describe something that you are still not clear about.

3. Examine the first four NCTM Curriculum Standards: Mathematics as problem Solving, Mathematics as Communication, Mathematics as Reasoning, and Mathematical Connections. Select one of the subheadings from this set that you feel you "own" more as a result of this exploration. Describe what you learned.

4. What did you learn about the use of measurement in experiments?

SECTION   2.3   **EXPLORING NUMERATION**

One day an elementary teacher, Georges Ifrah, was asked by one of his students, "How did numbers start? When did people learn to count?" At the time, all he could say was "I don't know" and "a long time ago." To answer those questions, he did quite a bit of research and wrote a fascinating book called *From One to Zero: A Universal History of Numbers.* Historical records show that many different kinds of number systems were created as humans' understanding of mathematics increased. You will spend some time creating your own numeration system so that you will be able to understand more deeply how we use numbers.

EXPLORATION 2.8   **Alphabitia**

Imagine that you are a member of a small tribe that lived thousands of years ago, when people were making the transition from being hunter-gatherers to becoming farmers. You have a numeration system that is alphabetically based, so you are called Alphabitians. Like many other ancient peoples your numeration system is finite. For any amount greater than Z, you have no symbol; you just call that amount "many."

PART 1: Inventing a new system

Now that your tribe has settled down, you have "many" sheep and "many" ears of corn. Without an adequate numeration system, figuring out how many more sheep you have this year than last year and determining each family's share of the corn harvest is very tedious. A young woman in your tribe has excitedly announced that she has invented a new counting system with which she can represent any amount using only the symbols A, B, C, D, and a new symbol she calls zero and writes as 0. Unfortunately for your tribe, this young woman died on a hunting trip. However, she left behind some artifacts that she was going to use to help you learn the new system. These artifacts are called flats, longs, and units.

Your tribe has a need for a new numeration system. Since the visionary member of your tribe is no longer with you, it is up to you to invent a new numeration system. That is, you need to develop a system that lets you represent any amount using only the symbols A, B, C, D, and 0.

1. Make your own artifacts from the cutout at the end of the book or cut out a number of flats, longs, and units from graph paper.

2. Take some time to sit down with your partners and create a numeration system using only the symbols A, B, C, D, and 0.

3. Some groups will find that one member proposes a system that makes sense to everyone quickly. Other groups will discuss and debate two or more systems before finally deciding on one system. After you have explored different alternatives, answer the following questions:

   a. Does your system make sense?

   b. Imagine that you will be explaining your system to the council of the elders. How would you explain your system to them?

   c. If your group decided among two or more possibilities, what made you choose one system over the other(s)?

PART 2: Communicating different systems

At a time specified by your instructor, each group will post its system on the wall, and each student will have time to look at the other systems.

1. Make a group poster. Each group's poster needs to contain the following:

   ■ The name of your new counting system (feel free to be creative and playful).

■ A table showing your symbols for at least the first Z numbers. You might want to add a third column to show pictures of your numbers and/or explanations for the readers to help them understand how your system works.

Old	New
A	
B	
C	
D	
E	
...	
X	
Y	
Z	

■ Directions that will help other students to understand the system (*Remember: You will not be there to explain it to other students.*)
■ A frank and honest assessment of the advantages and disadvantages or limitations of your new system

2. ***First discussion of the systems: observations and questions***   After students have had a chance to examine the different systems, there will be a class discussion in which you will be asked to share your observations and questions about other systems.

    a. Jot down observations or questions that you would like to remember.

    b. What did you learn from this discussion?

3. ***Taking different systems for a test drive***   After examining all the systems, select the two systems that you like best and take them for a "test drive." You may choose the system your group developed as one of the two systems. Each test drive must include the following tasks:

    a. Try counting up to double Z (that is, the amount equivalent to Z + Z in the original Alphabitian system). Record your symbols and describe any difficulties you had and any uncertainties you have. For example, you may see two reasonable possibilities for a certain amount.

    b. Make up and solve some simple story problems involving addition (e.g., new sheep born), subtraction (e.g., selling sheep), multiplication (e.g., planting rows of trees), and division (e.g., dividing ears of corn among several families). Please stay in your role as Alphabitians. Among other things, this means forgetting the computation procedures you know as Americans. Thus, when you divide, think how you (as an Alphabitian) might determine the answer to the question in your story problem.

    c. Evaluate each system. First, summarize its strengths and weaknesses or limitations. Then make any recommendations for improving the system.

4. *Second discussion of systems: choosing one system*   At this time, your class will decide upon one system that you will all learn and use. You might select one of the systems created, or you might combine two systems (each with certain advantages) and then select the combined system.

    a. As different students nominate a system and then debate the advantages and limitations of that system, make notes about any points that you want to remember.

    b. What did you learn from this discussion?

PART 3: Learning about the new system

1.   **a.** After the class selects the system that it will use, take time to learn that system. You may want to review the "4 Steps for Solving Problems" before you begin.

    b. Once your group feels that each member understands the new system, take a few moments to jot down tools that helped you.

For Steps 2 and 3, take some time to answer the following questions. Answer them using manipulatives, diagrams, or symbols.

2. What number comes after each of the following? Briefly explain how you answered each question.

    a. AA   **b.** BD   **c.** BAD   **d.** ABD

3. What number comes before each of the following? Briefly explain how you answered each question.

    a. D0   **b.** B00   **c.** D0D0

4. Compare your responses to Steps 2 and 3 with other members of your group.

Take some time to analyze mistakes. Were they just careless, or do they point to some aspects of this system about which you are still fuzzy?

Your instructor may have you do one or more additional worksheets.

Looking Back on Exploration 2.8

1. Describe the most important learnings from this exploration. In each case, first describe what it was that you learned and then describe how you learned it.

2. Describe something in this exploration that you are still not clear about.

3. Examine the first four NCTM Curriculum Standards: Mathematics as Problem Solving, Mathematics as Communication, Mathematics as Reasoning, and Mathematical Connections. Select one of the subheadings from this set that you feel you "own" more as a result of this exploration. Describe what you learned.

EXPLORATION 2.9   **Different Bases**

In this exploration, we will explore several different bases and their relationships to one another. The primary purpose of these explorations is to deepen your understanding of base 10 — that is, your understanding of place value and the function of zero. I have found that the structures of a system are often best seen by putting the familiar in an unfamiliar context; this was the reason for the Alphabitian exploration. Over the past ten years, I have observed that an increasing number of elementary teachers have their students explore different bases. These teachers have told me that the explorations with different bases help their students come to a better understanding of place value and how base 10 works, and that this knowledge translates to better problem-solving in base 10.

We will begin by exploring three different bases after noting an important caution: Working in different bases is often difficult at first. If you find yourself groping about, consider the following tools to help you:

Connections

Can I connect what I know about base 10 to this new base?

Problem-Solving Strategies

- What if I made a table? Would that help?
- As I make my tables, what patterns do I see?

  Transition numbers are often difficult; in base 10, for example, 99 is a transition number. When you encounter transition numbers, consider the following questions:

- Might it help to use manipulatives?
- Might it help to stop and say what the symbols mean?

Patterns

- Are there patterns that are true for all bases?
- Are there patterns that are true for some bases but not others?

You may have already surmised that the new Alphabitian system is actually a base 5 system that uses A, B, C, and D instead of 1, 2, 3, and 4. Before proceeding with the following explorations, you might want to make a base 5 counting chart (1, 2, 3, 4, 10, 11, 12, 13, 14, 20, 21 . . .) and become comfortable with this system.

PART 1: Learning about different bases

Base 6

The following activities are designed to help you understand base 6.

1. **a.** If your instructor has base 6 manipulatives, get them if you wish. If your instructor does not have them, you might want to make your own, using graph paper.

   b. Take some time, individually or in a group, to learn how to count in base 6.

   c. As you learn about this new base, remember to have a group check-in frequently to be sure you are not leaving anyone behind. One way to do this is to ask a question and see if everyone can answer it and explain it. For example, pick a number and ask what the next number is or what the previous number is. Record your work.

2. Once you have determined that all members of the group understand base 6, respond to the following questions.

   a. What helped you to accomplish this task?

   b. What patterns do you see in this base?

3. Now that you are able to count in base 6, try the following exercises, both to assess your understanding and to stretch your understanding. Answers are on page 43.

   a. What comes after each of the following?[2] 25_6 555_6 1235_6

---

[2] A subscript at the end of a number indicates the base. Thus, 25_6 means the amount 25 in base 6. When there is no subscript, the number is in base 10.

b. What comes before each of the following? 40_6 300_6 12340_6

4. Describe one area in which you had initial difficulty — for example, deciding what comes after 555_6. Describe the difficulty; for example, did you have no idea, or were you debating between two possible answers? Describe what it was that helped you get unstuck.

Base 2

The following activities are designed to help you understand base 2.

5. **a.** If your instructor has base 2 manipulatives, get them if you wish. If your instructor does not have them, you might want to make your own, using graph paper.

  b. Take some time, individually or in a group, to learn how to count in base 2.

  c. As you learn about base 2, remember to have a group check-in frequently, as in Step 1(c).

6. Once you have determined that all members of the group understand base 2, respond to the following questions:

  a. What helped you to accomplish this task?

  b. What patterns do you see in this base?

7. Now that you are able to count in base 2, try the following exercises, both to assess your understanding and to stretch your understanding. Answers are on page 44.

  a. What comes after each of the following? 110_2 1011_2 101111_2

  b. What comes before each of the following? 100_2 111_2 1010_2

8. Describe one area in which you had initial difficulty — for example, deciding what comes after 1011_2. Describe the difficulty; for example, did you have no idea, or were you debating between two possible answers? Describe what it was that helped you get unstuck.

9. Some students find base 2 the hardest to learn, whereas others find it the easiest. Why do you think this is so?

Base 12

The following activities are designed to help you learn about base 12.

10. **a.** If your instructor has base 12 manipulatives, get them if you wish. If your instructor does not have them, you might want to make your own, using graph paper.

   b. Take some time, individually or in a group, to learn how to count in base 12. Then read part (c).

   c. Base 12 presents a problem that did not come up in the other bases: How do you represent the amount that in base 10 is called "10" in base 12? What do you think? Write down your first thoughts.

   d. Discuss the problem in part (c) in your group. Discuss why this is a problem, and discuss possible ways to resolve it. Write down your thoughts.

11. **a.** Once you have resolved the problem of new digits, by consulting your instructor or from a class discussion, take some time, individually or together as a group, to learn how to count in base 12.

   b. As you learn about base 12, remember to have a group check-in frequently, as in Step 1(c).

12. Once you have determined that all members of the group understand base 12, respond to the following questions:

   a. What helped you to accomplish this task?

   b. What patterns do you see in this base?

13. Now that you are able to count in base 12, try the following exercises, both to assess your understanding and to stretch your understanding. Answers are on page 44.

   a. What comes after each of the following? 39_{12} $7E_{12}$ TTT_{12}

   b. What comes before each of the following? 100_{12} 450_{12} 1010_{12}

14. Describe one area in which you had initial difficulty — for example, deciding what comes after 19_{12}. Describe the difficulty; for example, did you have no idea, or were you debating between two possible answers? Describe what it was that helped you get unstuck.

PART 2: Similarities and differences among the bases

At this point, you can count in several different bases. In fact, if you stop to think for a moment, you could count in base 3 without further instruction, as long as you understand what it means to say base 3.

1. Take a minute to see if, indeed, you can count in base 3. If you can't, your understanding of bases may be primarily procedural, or "rented."

   When we examine bases, we find that certain rules or patterns are true for any base, but that other patterns occur in some, but not all, bases. This observation is the focus of this exploration.

2. Take some time to look at the different bases. What patterns do you see in all bases? What patterns do you see in some bases but not other bases? Record your observations in a table. Also note what sparked the discovery — perhaps looking at a table or hearing a comment by someone else.

Patterns common to all bases:	What sparked this discovery?
Patterns common to certain bases: (specify the bases)	What sparked this discovery?

3. Listen to other students describe their patterns. Write down the new patterns that you heard about.

Looking Back

Now that you have learned to count in many bases (you are multinumerate, as opposed to multilingual), take some time to reflect on what you have learned and then answer the following questions.

1.   To what extent did this exploration deepen your understanding of base 10?

2.   Describe one problem-solving tool that was particularly useful in these explorations. Your description needs to have enough specificity that the reader can see how that tool actually changed your understanding.

3.   What was the most important thing you learned from investigating different bases?

PART 3: Translating from another base into base 10

A traveler going from the United States to Great Britain has to convert dollars to pounds. Similarly, we will now investigate the process of converting amounts from one base to another. Before we proceed, I need to emphasize strongly that the point of the following explorations is not to master the procedure for translating from one base to another. Rather, these explorations have two aims: (1) to give you practice in applying the problem-solving tools you are developing, and (2) to deepen your understanding of base 10, which is the base that you will (at least implicitly) teach your future students, whether you are a kindergarten teacher helping your students learn to count, a second-grade teacher helping your students learn how to subtract, or a sixth-grade teacher helping your student learn decimals.

To help keep you focused on this goal and to make the process a bit more fun, let us go into the future and imagine that there are intelligent beings on every planet of the solar system. The beings on Mercury use what we call base 2; the beings on Venus use what we call base 5; the beings on Mars use what we call base 6; and the beings on Jupiter use what we call base 12.

1.   Each planet would say that *it* has base "10." Do you see why? Discuss this question among your group and then write down why each planet would say it has base "10." Imagine explaining this to a classmate who was not present for this discussion and whose initial reaction to the statement is a puzzled expression.

2.   The United Nations of the Solar System is having its monthly interplanetary meeting. You are the hotel clerk who is handling reservations. Unfortunately, the faxes that come from each planet contain numbers in that planet's own base. Thus, you have to determine how many rooms to reserve for each delegation.

   a.   The Mercury delegation says that it needs 1101 rooms. How many rooms will you reserve?

b. The Venus delegation says that it needs 34 rooms. How many rooms will you reserve?

c. The Mars delegation says that it needs 23 rooms. How many rooms will you reserve?

d. The Jupiter delegation says that it needs 18 rooms. How many rooms will you reserve?

3. Think about how you translated from each of these bases into base 10. Develop an algorithm that can be used for each of the bases, using the following guidelines. Imagine that you are going home soon, and that the night clerk is not very confident with different bases. Write directions for this clerk so that she can make the appropriate number of reservations, regardless of which base is used. At the same time, imagine that the night clerk is curious and wants to understand. Draw a line down the middle of the page. On the left, describe what to do. On the right, explain why this works; in other words, justify each step in the algorithm.

4. Now imagine that the United Nations of the Solar System is having its biannual interplanetary conference. The number of participants at this conference is much greater than for the monthly meeting. As before, imagine that you are the clerk and need to reserve the appropriate number of rooms.

   a. The Mercury delegation says that it needs 100110 rooms. How many rooms will you reserve?

   b. The Venus delegation says that it needs 403 rooms. How many rooms will you reserve?

   c. The Mars delegation says that it needs 203 rooms. How many rooms will you reserve?

   d. The Jupiter delegation says that it needs 109 rooms. How many rooms will you reserve?

5. Once your group is confident that you have reserved the correct number of rooms, take a moment to look back on what you have learned. Did your algorithm from Step 3 work for larger numbers? That is, did it stretch well or

did it break down? If it did not stretch well, explain the new algorithm that you developed.

PART 4: Translating from base 10 into other bases

1.   The United Nations of Earth has held new elections, and it is time to send the new delegations to each of the planets. You are in charge of sending a fax to each planet telling them how many people are in the new delegation. However, you realize that the person who receives the message may not translate accurately from our base into their base. So you have decided that you will tell them the number of people in the delegation in their system. Below are the numbers of people in the delegation to each planet in base 10.

   a.   The delegation to Mercury will consist of 34 people. Translate this amount into the base used on Mercury.

   b.   The delegation to Venus will consist of 34 people. Translate this amount into the base used on Venus.

   c.   The delegation to Mars will consist of 34 people. Translate this amount into the base used on Mars.

   d.   The delegation to Jupiter will consist of 34 people. Translate this amount into the base used on Jupiter.

2.   Think about how you translated from base 10 into each of these bases. Develop an algorithm that can be used for each of the bases, using the following guidelines. Imagine that you need to give directions to the person who will send faxes from the United Nations of Earth to each of the planets after the next elections. Draw a line down the middle of the page. On the left, describe what to do. On the right, explain why that works; in other words, justify each step in the algorithm.

3.   Now imagine that you are a travel agent on Earth handling reservations for tours to each of these planets. You need to reserve the appropriate number of rooms.

   a.   The tour to Mercury has 208 people. Translate this amount into the base used on Mercury.

   b.   The tour to Venus has 208 people. Translate this amount into the base used on Venus.

c. The tour to Mars has 208 people. Translate this amount into the base used on Mars.

d. The tour to Jupiter has 208 people. Translate this amount into the base used on Jupiter.

4. Once your group is confident that you have reserved the correct number of rooms, take a moment to look back on what you have learned. Did your algorithm from Step 2 work for larger numbers? That is, did it stretch well, or did it break down?

Looking Back on Exploration 2.9

1. Describe the most important things that you learned while translating to and from base 10. In each case, first describe what it was that you learned and then describe how you learned it.

2. Describe something from this exploration that you are still not clear about.

3. Examine the first four NCTM Curriculum Standards: Mathematics as Problem Solving, Mathematics as Communication, Mathematics as Reasoning, and Mathematical Connections. Select one of the subheadings from this set that you feel you "own" better as a result of this exploration. Describe what you learned.

EXPLORATION 2.10   **A Place-Value Game**

Materials

- A six-sided die in which the 6 is covered with a zero
- A board with spaces for a 4-digit number, a 3-digit number, a 2-digit number, and a 1-digit number (shown on page 42)

Rules for competitive version

1. Each player has a separate score sheet.
2. After each roll of the die, players decide where on the score sheet to write the number.
3. After 10 rolls, each player determines the sum of the four numbers, that is, the 4-digit, 3-digit, 2-digit, and 1-digit numbers. The person with the largest sum wins.

1. Play the first game as follows:

    a. Do not speak during the game.

b. Record the order of the ten throws of your die. For example, 5 3 4 0 2 4 5 2 3 4.

— — — — — — — — — —

c. After the first game, take some time to think about your choices. Also think about whether you learned something from playing the game or from watching the other player. Can you express what you learned in a way that would make sense to someone who has not played the game? Write down the strategies that you learned from the first game.

2. Play the second game as follows:

a. Record the order of the ten throws of your die.

— — — — — — — — — —

b. Every time you write a number in the grid, explain why you chose that location.

c. After the game, reflect on your strategy. Describe the strategies you learned from playing the second game or from watching the other player.

Looking Back on Exploration 2.10

1. Summarize your strategies for this game, and briefly justify them.

2. What did you learn from playing this game?

Looking Back

You have done several explorations (in class or on your own) during the course of this chapter.

1. Take a few minutes to think back on those explorations. What did you learn? Jot down your thoughts before reading on.

Now let us take some time to reflect on some specific things you have learned.

2. Select one problem-solving tool on which you feel you have made the most progress during this chapter. You may pick one from the "4 Steps for Solving Problems," or you may describe a tool you used that is not on that list.

    a. Give the tool a name. If it is a tool that is mentioned in the book, you can use that name, but you are encouraged to use a name that describes your own perspective.

    b. Show *how* you used that tool to solve a problem. Imagine describing this tool to readers who do not yet have this tool in their repertoire. How can you help the readers to see not just *what* you did but also *how* you solved the problem so that they can get a sense of how this tool works?

3. Many students enter this course not knowing how to check their answers, other than by checking their computation. What have you learned about being able to "verify and interpret results with respect to the original problem" in the course of these explorations?

4. In what ways have these explorations helped you to you feel more "confidence in using mathematics meaningfully"?

5. We want students to be able to "justify their answers and solution processes." Again, this idea is new for many students. In what ways has having to justify your answers and solution processes — to the instructor on an assignment, to a group member in a discussion, and to yourself while working on a problem — helped to make you a stronger learner of mathematics?

6. Although the use of patterns is included as one of the major problem-solving tools, it also appears in Standard 3 (Mathematics as Reasoning): we want students to be able to "use patterns and relationships to analyze mathematical situations." In what ways have these explorations helped you to *see* patterns better? For example, did you find that seeing and then analyzing a pattern (using reasoning, tables, etc.) was a key to solving one of the problems?

Answers to Exploration questions
Exploration 2.9: Base 6, p. 34

30_6 comes after 25_6. 1000_6 comes after 555_6. 1240_6 comes after 1235_6.
35_6 comes before 40_6. 255_6 comes before 300_6. 12335_6 comes before 12340_6.

Exploration 2.9: Base 2, p. 35

111_2 comes after 110_2. 1100_2 comes after 1011_2. 110000_2 comes after 101111_2.

11_2 comes before 100_2. 110_2 comes before 111_2. 1001_2 comes before 1010_2.

Exploration 2.21: Base 12, p. 36

$3T_{12}$ comes after 39_{12}. 80_{12} comes after $7E_{12}$. TTE_{12} comes after TTT_{12}.

EE_{12} comes before 100_{12}. $44E_{12}$ comes before 450_{12}. $100E_{12}$ comes before 1010_{12}.

3

The Four Fundamental Operations of Arithmetic

I n Chapter 2, you explored three fundamental concepts of the elementary school curriculum: sets, function, and numeration. As Alphabitians you constructed a numeration system that is much more powerful than early numeration systems, and you gained a deeper understanding of the concepts of base, place value, and the role of zero in this system. This chapter builds on that knowledge so that you can see how our numeration system connects to the fundamental operations of addition, subtraction, multiplication, and division. Understanding these connections will help you develop "operation sense," which in turn will help you with mental arithmetic—doing computations in your head—and estimation.

SECTION   3.1   **EXPLORING ADDITION AND SUBTRACTION**

Can you remember learning to add and subtract in first and second grade? As adults you probably don't think twice about adding and subtracting, but these operations are often difficult for many youngsters, especially when regrouping is involved. One way to help you better understand what these operations mean is to have you do problems in a different setting.

In Chapter 2 you put yourself in the role of a member of the Alphabitian tribe (Exploration 2.8), and in that role you created a numeration system. You will be asked to remain Alphabitians for a while longer and add and subtract in that system.

EXPLORATION 3.1   **Inventing and Understanding Addition in Alphabitia**

1. Make up and solve at least two addition story problems in Alphabitia and then discuss in your group how you solved them. Respond to the following questions:

    a. What knowledge of counting, place value, and bases did you use and need to know?

    b. What difficulties did you encounter?

    c. What knowledge or tool(s) got you past the difficulty?

2. Stop and reflect a moment on the story problems you did, and write your response to the following question: What does addition mean?

3. Now let us explore and understand how we might find the sums when the numbers are larger. It may surprise you to learn that the algorithms for addition, subtraction, multiplication, and division that you learned in elementary school are not the only possible algorithms. Over the centuries, many different algorithms have been invented, and even today, children in some countries and some parts of the United States learn different algorithms. You will investigate some of these other algorithms in the textbook.

    A major goal in the explorations in this section and the next section is for you to be able to determine sums, differences, products, and quotients in ways that make sense to you and that you can justify (that is, you can explain why they work). In so doing, some of you will actually reinvent algorithms that were invented by other people, or you may even invent a totally new algorithm!

    a. Now try these Alphabitian problems:

    $$\begin{array}{r} BB \\ +CC \\ \hline \end{array} \qquad \begin{array}{r} BC \\ +CD \\ \hline \end{array}$$

    b. What knowledge of counting, place value, and bases did you use and need to know?

    c. What difficulties did you encounter?

    d. What knowledge or tool(s) got you past the difficulty?

4.   Describe and justify your procedure for adding Alphabitian numbers. Imagine explaining how to add to an Alphabitian elder who has learned to count but who has no idea how to add "big numbers."

5.   Now let us examine some addition problems with larger numbers. Focus on making sense of the process, not simply on "getting" the procedure.

   a.   Do the following problems according to your instructor's directions.

BCD	B0B	C0D	D0D0
+DB	+ABC	+CAB	+BABA

   b.   Compare your solution path with those of other students in your group and explain your process. Your goal in this discussion is to understand how each group member made sense of the problem in order to successfully find the sum.

   c.   After you have heard about each person's solution path, stop and reflect on what differences you note. For example, did some use manipulatives, or solve the problems using diagrams, and did some do the problems without manipulatives or diagrams? Did some start at the left and work to the right, and did some start at the right (ones place) and move left? Note any differences that stand out.

EXPLORATION 3.2   **Exploring Patterns in Alphabitian Addition**

Being able to add large numbers easily not only requires an understanding of how our numeration system works but also requires that the "addition facts" be internalized. For example, if you have to stop and figure out what B + C is when adding ACDB + B0CC, the process will be slow. Many young children simply learn addition facts by rote. However, there are many, many patterns in mathematics, and these patterns can also be used to help children learn addition facts. One important exploration that will help you internalize addition facts is to make an addition table and then recognize and analyze patterns.

1.   **a.**   Make an addition table for adding in Alphabitia.

   b.   Compare your addition tables with those of others in your group. Is there a "right" size? If you were a teacher, what size addition table would you want your children to make? Justify your choice.

c. List all the patterns you observe in the table.

d. Listen to other group members describe the patterns that they observed. Add any that didn't appear on your list.

2. Describe patterns.

a. Describe one pattern as if you were talking on the phone to a person who was not in class today. Assume that the person has an addition table.

b. Exchange descriptions with a member of your group. Pretend that you were not in class today and give feedback to the other person with respect to the accuracy and clarity of that person's statement.

3. Now learn Alphabitian addition facts.

a. Are there any facts that are harder to learn than others? If so, describe what makes them hard.

b. What helps you remember addition facts, such as C + B = A0?

c. If you were going to have a quiz on Alphabitian addition facts, what patterns would help you remember them?

4. This problem has missing digits: B_D + C_ = CBB.

a. Figure out the missing digits alone and show your work.

b. Compare your solution paths and answers with those of other members of your group. Note here new strategies and ideas that you would like to remember.

EXPLORATION 3.3 **Exploring Subtraction in Alphabitia**

1. As you probably discovered in Explorations 3.1 and 3.2, there are different ways in which we can represent and solve addition problems. So too for subtraction problems. Make up two Alphabitian subtraction story problems and solve them. Solve them in a way that makes sense to you—by using manipulatives, diagrams, or numerals. Have at least one of the problems involve regrouping. Focus on making sense of the process, not on "getting" it.

2. **a.** Which problem was more difficult?

b. What was hard about the problem?

c. What previous knowledge (about numeration systems, place value, addition, and so on) did you need to solve the problem?

d. How confident are you that your answer is correct? Explain.

3. Just as you found that there are different kinds of Alphabitian addition problems, there are different kinds of subtraction problems.

a. List all the subtraction problems made up by the members of your group. Then classify the problems according to type. That is, put problems that feel similar into the same group.

b. Name and describe each group. The key idea here is for you to look for patterns, similarities, and differences rather than "doing it right."

c. Now write your response to the following question: What does subtraction mean?

4. Take some time to solve those of the subtraction problems below that your instructor assigns. Solve the problems in a way that *makes sense* to you—by using manipulatives, diagrams, or numerals. If you use manipulatives, draw pictures to record your solution process.

The goal here is to be able to determine the difference in a way that makes sense to you; there is no one right way to solve these problems. Check each answer before moving on.

a. $\begin{array}{r} DB \\ -AD \\ \hline \end{array}$ **b.** $\begin{array}{r} D0 \\ -BB \\ \hline \end{array}$ **c.** $\begin{array}{r} CBD \\ -ADC \\ \hline \end{array}$ **d.** $\begin{array}{r} DCB \\ -ABD \\ \hline \end{array}$

e. $\begin{array}{r} C00 \\ -BAB \\ \hline \end{array}$ **f.** $\begin{array}{r} D00 \\ -\ B0B \\ \hline \end{array}$ **g.** $\begin{array}{r} C0B \\ -BAD \\ \hline \end{array}$ **h.** $\begin{array}{r} A00 \\ -\ CA \\ \hline \end{array}$

i. $\begin{array}{r} B0A \\ -\ BD \\ \hline \end{array}$ **j.** $\begin{array}{r} B0AC \\ -\ BCD \\ \hline \end{array}$ **k.** $\begin{array}{r} A0B0C \\ -\ B0CA \\ \hline \end{array}$ **l.** $\begin{array}{r} A0B00 \\ -\ D0B \\ \hline \end{array}$

5. Compare your solution path for each problem with those of other members of your group. If some people solved a problem using methods different from yours, can you understand what they did? This is important, because if we honor their intelligence, young children will invent all sorts of interesting ways to solve problems. Many of my students have invented procedures that I have read about in history books.

6. a. Most of you were taught to "carry" and "borrow." That language is discouraged these days. Why do you think this is so?

   b. Discuss this matter with your group and write down your group's response. Think of it as a first draft rather than as something that has to be "right."

   c. After listening to other groups' responses, write a second draft response to the question.

   d. List possible alternative terms.

   e. After hearing other students' suggestions and rationale, select the words that you would use, and then justify your choices.

Looking Back

You have developed your own algorithms for adding and subtracting in Alphabitia, and you have explored other algorithms. Take some time now to reflect on the following questions:

1. What did you learn about addition and subtraction from inventing your own ways of determining the sums or differences?

2. Do you understand the standard algorithms better? If so, what do you understand better now than you did before?

3. Explain how adding and subtracting are connected. Use diagrams and words.

4. When the teacher asked how borrowing and carrying are connected, Uri said, "They are the same process." What is the same about them?

SECTION 3.2 **EXPLORING MULTIPLICATION AND DIVISION**

The concepts of and algorithms for multiplication and division are more complex than those for addition and subtraction. Therefore, we will leave the Alphabitians and explore multiplication and division in base 10. It is crucial that your understanding of multiplication and division be richer than simply knowing how to multiply and how to divide.

EXPLORATION 3.4 **Multiplication from Different Perspectives**

There are many perspectives from which to explore multiplication. We will look at three of them in this exploration.

Skip Counting

Multiplication is often introduced to children as skip counting, that is, counting by 2, by 3, by 4, and so on. A common activity in second grade is to look for patterns in skip counting. This activity is fun and rewarding for college students also. The worksheet entitled "Patterns in Multiples" contains counting tables that make it easier to skip-count. In the steps below you will color in the multiples of each of the numbers from 2 through 9 in these worksheets.

1. First look at each worksheet and predict what it will look like after you color in the multiples of the appropriate number. Do this as a group until you come to a consensus on a prediction or until you find that you cannot make a prediction or you have different predictions. Write any predictions in the following table.

2. Color the charts and describe the pattern(s) you see. If the appearance of the chart is different from your prediction, you might understand why. If this happens, describe your insight.

3. After you have predicted and then colored in the chart, describe any patterns that you see in the actual numbers. For example, all multiples of 2 have an even number in the ones place. If you do see something, describe the insight.

Multiples of 2: **predicted appearance:** **actual appearance:** **insights:**	
Multiples of 3: **predicted appearance:** **actual appearance:** **insights:**	
Multiples of 4: **predicted appearance:** **actual appearance:** **insights:**	

Multiples of 5: **predicted appearance:** **actual appearance:** **insights:**	
Multiples of 6: **predicted appearance:** **actual appearance:** **insights:**	
Multiples of 7: **predicted appearance:** **actual appearance:** **insights:**	
Multiples of 8: **predicted appearance:** **actual appearance:** **insights:**	
Multiples of 9: **predicted appearance:** **actual appearance:** **insights:**	

4.   Now that you have colored in eight different charts, describe any patterns you see among the charts. For example, some patterns appear in all of the charts; some patterns occur in only one or some of the charts. If you have any hypotheses about the reasons for this, write them now.

Multiplication from an Algebraic Perspective

In Step 4 above, we found that some multiples have a vertical pattern, other multiples have diagonal patterns, and still others have both. Let us focus on these patterns from an algebraic perspective as lines and examine the slopes of these lines. (A line's slope is the ratio of its vertical change to its horizontal change.)

5.   Determine the slopes of the lines that you see in each table. Let each cell in a table count as one unit.

6.   What patterns and connections do you see? For example, do certain charts have similar slopes? Why? Can you explain these patterns; for example, why is 1/2, and not 1/3 or 1/4, the slope of one family of lines in the multiples of 8? Write down your explanation.1

Multiplication from a Geometric Perspective

Now let us look at multiplication and the multiplication table from a geometric perspective. (A multiplication table is shown in Exploration 3.5.) This exploration comes from an article in *Teaching Children Mathematics*,[1] a journal you will want to subscribe to as soon as possible. Using graph paper, you will make a grid for each cell in the multiplication table up to 10 × 10. For example, 3 × 2 will be ⊞. You may want to make the entire set of grids yourself, or your instructor may ask each group to construct one master set of grids.

7. Whether you make the grids alone or in a group, discuss strategies that will enable you to complete the set of grids more efficiently.

8. Once you have the completed set, "play" with the grids, physically and mentally. Describe any mathematical insights and patterns that you see from your exploration.

EXPLORATION 3.5 **Patterns in the Multiplication Table**

PART 1: Base 10

1. Examine the multiplication table and describe at least three patterns that you see.

	1	2	3	4	5	6	7	8	9	10	11	12
1	1	2	3	4	5	6	7	8	9	10	11	12
2	2	4	6	8	10	12	14	16	18	20	22	24
3	3	6	9	12	15	18	21	24	27	30	33	36
4	4	8	12	16	20	24	28	32	36	40	44	48
5	5	10	15	20	25	30	35	40	45	50	55	60
6	6	12	18	24	30	36	42	48	54	60	66	72
7	7	14	21	28	35	42	49	56	63	70	77	84
8	8	16	24	32	40	48	56	64	72	80	88	96
9	9	18	27	36	45	54	63	72	81	90	99	108
10	10	20	30	40	50	60	70	80	90	100	110	120
11	11	22	33	44	55	66	77	88	99	110	121	132
12	12	24	36	48	60	72	84	96	108	120	132	144

[1] Barbara E. Armstrong, "Teaching Patterns, Relationships, and Multiplication as Worthwhile Mathematical Tasks", *Teaching Children Mathematics*, 1(7) (1995), pp. 446–450.

2. Select one pattern that your group will share with the class.

   a. Describe this pattern, as if you were talking on the phone to a friend who missed class today but who has a multiplication table handy. The purpose of your description is simply to get the person to see the pattern.

   b. Exchange descriptions with another group. If they easily interpreted your description, great. If not, revise your description (like a second draft of an essay). Discuss the parts of your description that were not clear to the other group. That is, what was unclear about them, and why do you think the revised wording is better?

   c. What did you learn from describing a pattern and reading another group's description?

3. Now explain *why* the pattern occurs.

PART 2: Circle clocks

Circle clocks (also called star patterns) have been used by many teachers over the course of many years to introduce many different mathematical concepts and to provide a visual connection for these ideas. The following steps use these circle clocks to give you another perspective on the basic multiplication facts.

Take out the Base 10 Circle Clocks from the end of the book. You will draw on one clock for each of the rows in the multiplication table from 2 through 9. The directions are to look only at the units digit. For example, if we look at the multiplication facts in row 2 and write down only the units digit, we have: 2, 4, 6, 8, 0, and then the numbers repeat. Start your pencil at 2 on the circle, then draw a line from 2 to 4, then from 4 to 6, and so on.

1. Complete the circle clock for the multiples of 2, and describe the pattern as if you were talking to someone on the phone.

2. Complete the circle clocks for each of the other multiples.

3. What similarities do you see among the different circle clocks? Can you explain why those similarities occur?

4. Predict the shape of the circle clock for the multiples of 11. Explain your reasoning. Then draw the pattern. If your prediction was correct, great. If it wasn't, or if you weren't able to make a prediction, either describe the knowledge that you weren't able to apply or describe what enables you to understand why the pattern is what it is.

PART 3: Other bases

Make a set of multiplication tables in different bases determined by your class or your instructor.

1.   What similarities do you see among these tables? Describe patterns that are true in all bases and patterns that are true in some but not all bases.

2.   Describe patterns that are true in only one base.

3.   Do you have hypotheses for any of the patterns?

EXPLORATION 3.6   **Algorithms for Multiplying**

Before the introduction of the Arabic notation, multiplication was difficult, and the division even of integers called into play the highest mathematical faculties. Probably nothing in the modern world could have more astonished a Greek mathematician than to hear that, under the influence of compulsory education, the whole population of Western Europe . . . could perform the operation of division for the largest numbers. This fact would have seemed . . . a sheer impossibility.[2]

PART 1: Egyptian duplation

How do you think people multiplied before base 10? Imagine finding 35×28 with the Egyptian numerals we saw in Section 2.3 of the text, that is, ∩∩∩||||| times ∩∩||||||||. The Egyptians, who did not have a numeration system with a base, developed an algorithm for multiplying based on the idea of multiplication as repeated addition and using doubling. This was the most practical way to multiply in the Western world before base 10 was adopted.

The Egyptians did the following:

∩∩∩||||| 35
∩∩∩∩∩∩∩   70
𝟿∩∩∩∩   140
𝟿𝟿∩∩∩∩∩∩∩∩   280
𝟿𝟿𝟿𝟿𝟿∩∩∩∩∩   560

You might be able to figure out the Egyptian method more easily if you use Hindu-Arabic numerals.

The Egyptians would then add

𝟿∩∩∩∩   140
𝟿𝟿∩∩∩∩∩∩∩∩   280
𝟿𝟿𝟿𝟿𝟿∩∩∩∩∩   +560

to come up with

𝟿𝟿𝟿𝟿𝟿𝟿𝟿𝟿𝟿∩∩∩∩∩∩∩∩

To get 35×28, add

140
280
+560
980

[2] Alfred North Whitehead, *Introduction to Mathematics*, New York, 1911, p. 59, cited in Robert Moritz, *On Mathematics* (New York: Dover Publications, 1914), p. 198.

1. Working alone or with a partner, determine how this algorithm works. Write directions for multiplying using this method.

2. Why does this method work?

3. What mathematics do you have to know in order to be able to use this method?

PART 2: Understanding the standard multiplication algorithm

Using your understanding of our base 10 numeration system and your understanding that multiplication can be seen both as repeated addition and as a rectangular array, you can now understand *why* our modern multiplication algorithm works. We will begin by examining simple multiplication problems and then gradually work up to bigger ones.

1. What if you forgot what 8×7 was? Describe two different ways in which you could figure it out that would be quicker than adding 7 eight times or adding 8 seven times. After the class discussion, describe other ways that you like.

2. For each of the problems below, assume that you only know multiplication facts up to 10×10.

   a. Describe how you could determine 13×7. After the class discussion, describe other ways that you like.

   b. Describe how you could determine 17×12. After the class discussion, describe other ways that you like.

   c. Describe how you could determine 19×13. After the class discussion, describe other ways that you like.

   d. Describe how you could determine 34×23. After the class discussion, describe other ways that you like.

3. Using the graph paper at the end of the book, represent 34×23 as a rectangle. Determine the answer using the idea of covering this amount with base 10 blocks—first flats, then longs, then units. Look at how you determined the product and then look at how you determine the product using the standard algorithm (the usual multiplication method). Now describe any new insights you have about why the algorithm works.

4. Using the problem below, explain why each step in the standard multiplication algorithm works.

$$\begin{array}{r} 56 \\ \times\ 37 \\ \hline 392 \\ 168 \\ \hline 2072 \end{array}$$

a. We begin by multiplying 7 and 6. How do we know to multiply these two digits and not, for example, 5 and 6?

b. Then, instead of placing the product (42) below, we place only the 2 below. Why is this?

c. Next, we find the product of 5 and 7. Why are we doing this step next?

d. Then we add the 4 from the previous step to the 35 we get from 5 times 7, and we place the 39 to the left of the original 2. What does this 392 represent?

e. Next we multiply 3 and 6. How do we know to multiply these two digits?

f. Why don't we place the 8 from this multiplication under the 2 instead of the 9? That is, why do we "move over"?

g. Finally, we add 392 and 168. If this is multiplication, then why are we adding? What do those numbers represent?

EXPLORATION 3.7   **Connecting Multiplication and Number Sense**

We have spent some time developing an understanding of how the standard multiplication algorithm works. Another related need is to begin to connect the algorithms to the idea of place value, which, as we discovered in Chapter 2, is an essential characteristic of our Hindu-Arabic numeration system. This exploration is powerful for many students, for it helps to develop some of the number sense that is so needed when solving real-world problems.

Part 1: Which combination makes the biggest product?

1. Let's say that you have five 9s and you want to combine them, using only multiplication, to make the largest product. To the right are six different possible ways to combine them. Which of these combinations do you think will give you the largest product? Without doing the actual computations, make a hypothesis and explain the reasoning behind your hypothesis.

    $\square \times \square \times \square \times \square \times \square$

    $\square\square \times \square \times \square \times \square$

    $(\square\square \times \square\square) \times \square$

    $\square\square\square \times \square \times \square$

    $\square\square\square \times \square\square$

    $\square\square\square\square \times \square$

2. Before determining the actual products, share your hypothesis with other members of your group. After listening to the reasoning of others, if you change your mind, explain why you changed your mind and why you think the new combination will produce the greatest product.

3. Now determine the six products. Whether your hypothesis was right or wrong, can you explain why, in terms of place value, one product is greater than the others?

PART 2: Where do the digits go to make the biggest product?

This exploration is to be done with a partner. The object is to place the digits 1, 2, 3, 4, and 5 in the boxes to obtain the greatest product.

$$\begin{array}{r} \square\;\square\;\square \\ \times \quad \square\;\square \\ \hline \end{array}$$

In this part, we will be using guess–check–revise.

1. With your partner, take a few moments to decide upon your first guess. Briefly write your reasoning for your guess. Stop and think what digit you want in the hundreds place, and whether it matters which digits go in the two tens places and which digits go in the two ones places.

2. Determine the product longhand; do not use a calculator. Then stop and reflect on this guess. Did you learn anything from the guess?

3. Now take a few moments to decide upon your second guess. Write your second guess, and briefly write your reasoning for this guess.

4. Continue this process until you feel that you have found the combination that produces the greatest product.

5. Merge with another pair. If you have the same combination, share with each other (and then write) strategies that helped and what you have learned. If one pair has a greater product, have that pair share their reasoning that led to that hypothesis.

6. Merge with another group of four or join the whole class, according to your instructor's directions, to discuss the problem. Write what you learned from the discussion.

EXPLORATION 3.8   **Different Models of Division**

1. Make up a story problem for $15 \div 3$. Assume that you are a young child who does not yet know division. Describe how you would determine the answer. You may use pictures, but you are not required to.

2. Compare your stories with those of other members of your group. Just as we found that there are different models for addition, subtraction, and multiplication, there are different models for division.

    a. Sort your stories into two or more groups. Explain the common characteristic(s) of the stories in each group.

    b. Give a name to each of the groups and briefly justify that name.

    c. After listening to the class discussion, name and briefly define each of the models for division.

3. Consider the problem $92 \div 4$. Make up a story problem for these numbers that fits each of your models. Still assuming that you don't know the formal idea of division, describe how you would determine the answer.

EXPLORATION 3.9   **Connecting Models of Division to Two Division Algorithms**

PART 1: Understanding the standard algorithm

Consider the following story problem: There are three fifth-grade classrooms. The janitor has taken all of the desks out of the classrooms, has waxed the floors, and is now ready to put the desks back in the classrooms. The only problem is that he has forgotten how many go into each classroom. If there are 72 desks, how many go into each classroom?

1. Assuming that you don't know the long division algorithm, solve this problem with base 10 blocks in small groups. If disagreements arise, discuss them.

2. Now solve this problem using the long division algorithm you would usually use. Can you connect each step of the algorithm to a physical movement of the blocks? Do so in a display like the one below.

24 ⟌ 3)72 6 12 12	Algorithm	Blocks
	a. 3 "gazinta" 7 two times.	a.
	b. Place the 2 above the 7.	b.
	c. $3 \times 2 = 6$. Place the 6 below the 7.	c.
	d. Subtract (take away) 6 from 7.	d.
	e. Bring down the 2.	e.
	f. 3 "gazinta" 12 four times.	f.
	g. Place the 4 above the 2.	g.
	h. $3 \times 4 = 12$. Place the 12 below the other 12.	h.

3. Now let us examine a larger problem: A company has received 252 computers and will ship the same number to each of its 4 stores. How many computers does each store get? The middle column of the table below contains selected steps in the algorithm. The right column asks you to justify the step.

63 ⟌ 4)252 24 12 12	Algorithm	Justification
	a. 4 doesn't go into 2.	a. What is going on mathematically here?
	b. 4 goes into 25 six times.	b. What is going on mathematically here?
	c. $4 \times 6 = 24$; put the 6 above the 5.	c. How do you know where to put the 6?
	d. Subtract 24 from 25.	d. Why are we subtracting?
	e. Bring down the 2.	e. What does this mean mathematically?

4. Many students have trouble when there are zeros in the quotient. Explain these four points in the long division problem below.

304 ⟌ 27)8208 81 108 108	Algorithm	Justification
	a. $27 \times 3 = 81$; put the 3 above the 2.	a. How do you know where to put the 3?
	b. Subtract $82 - 81$ and bring down the 0.	b. Why do we bring down the 0, since we are bringing down nothing?
	c. Since 27 doesn't go into 10, put a 0 above the 0.	c. Why?
	d. Bring down the 8.	d. Why?

PART 2: An alternative algorithm

Many students have trouble with long division. Common problems are poor multiplication facts, not being able to remember the sequence (divide, multiply, subtract, bring down), and misplacing the digits in the quotient. The standard long division algorithm can be unforgiving, as the example below shows. After repeated failure with the standard algorithm, many students simply give up; many of my students in this course have told me of bad experiences learning the division algorithm.

```
      69 R 24
  8)576
    48
    ──
    96
    72
    ──
    24
```

An alternative algorithm, called the scaffolding algorithm, has been helpful in giving students a sense of success, which builds their confidence. It also develops their ability to use guess–check–revise and reinforces their multiplication skills.

Here is how it might work with the problem 576 ÷ 8, which might represent 576 students grouped into 8 teams or 576 oranges divided into bags with 8 oranges per bag. In the former case, the student is asked, About how many students do you think would be on each team? In the second case, the student is asked, About how many bags do you think you can make?

Let's say the student's first guess is 60 — that is, 60 students per team or 60 bags of oranges. The student multiplies 60 × 8 to see how many students or oranges have been "used up" and how many are left to be dealt with. The 60 is placed at the top.

The student is now asked the same question with the remaining 96. Let's say the student guesses 10. The 10 is placed above the 60 (that is, in the "answer" space), and the student takes away the 10 groups of 8, or 80.

We now have 16 (students or oranges) to deal with. The student sees that 8 × 2 = 16 and places the 2 in the answer space. The student now adds 60 + 10 + 2 to get the answer.

At the far right is another example of this algorithm; note that the actual numbers in the answer space depend on the student's guess.

```
                                                          1
                                 2                         6
                   10           10                        20
        60         60           60                        50
    8)576      8)576        8)576                  64)4953
      480        480          480                     3200
      ───        ───          ───                     ────
       96         96           96                     1753
                  80           80                     1280
                  ──           ──                     ────
                  16           16                      473
                  16           16                      384
                  ──           ──                     ────
                   0            0                       89
                                                       64
                                                       ──
                                                       25
```

1.   Make up some long division problems and use the scaffolding algorithm to determine the quotient. Then explain why the scaffolding algorithm works.

2.   What advantages might this algorithm have in teaching?

3. Why do you think this algorithm is called the scaffolding algorithm?

EXPLORATION 3.10 **Dealing with Remainders**

Real-life problems involving division generally require not just the ability to do the computation but also the ability to interpret the result. This exploration enables you to explore the issue of remainders more deeply.

1. The Allentown Elementary School is going to the Science Museum in a nearby city. There are 369 students going, and each school bus can hold 24 students. How many school buses will be needed? Do this problem by yourself and then discuss your answer with members of your group.

2. Make up a story problem involving 31 divided by 4 in which the answer is

   a. 7   **b.** 8   **c.** $7\frac{3}{4}$ **d.** 7 remainder 3

3. After listening to other students' story problems, what did you learn about division from this exploration?

Looking Back

As you look back on the explorations with addition, subtraction, multiplication, and division, stop and reflect on what you have learned.

1. Briefly describe at least three important learnings. Below are four questions to start the reflection process.

- Did you learn more about what one or more of the operations means?
- Do you better understand how one or more of the algorithms work?
- Do you better understand how two or more of the operations are connected?
- Did working through these explorations cause you to understand place value more deeply or to understand how zero works in base 10?

2. Select and discuss one of these learnings. Your discussion needs to contain these three aspects:

   a. A description of *what* you learned

   b. Within this description, an explanation of the "why" behind the "what"

   c. An explanation of why this learning feels important to you

EXPLORATION 3.11   **Developing Operation Sense: String Art**

Many real-life problems are what NCTM calls "nonroutine, multistep problems," that is, problems that require more than one operation. In many of these situations, it is not obvious which operation to use. Unfortunately, many students have learned "tricks" that help them decide what operation to use—for example, "*of* means multiply," "if you see the word *more,* then subtract the numbers," and so on. These next explorations contain problems that require various operations and require you to apply your understanding of the operations in a nonroutine way: they require thinking as opposed to remembering tricks.

An elementary teacher, we'll call him Stanley, has found out about string art and has made a string art sculpture like the one below.

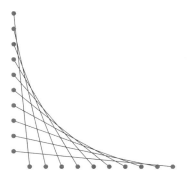

1. **a.** What do you see in the design?

    b. Make a copy of the design. Share your strategy for making the design with other members of your group. Did some members find ways to make the drawing that were easier than the ways others found?

    c. Having made the drawing yourself, do you see anything in the design that you didn't see before?

    d. If you were going to make a new design of your own, what would you like to try?

2. Suppose Stanley wants his whole class to make these sculptures.
    a. How many nails will he need for a class of 24 students?

    b. If the nails are 1 inch apart, how much string will he need?

c. Stanley wants to use four different colors of tapestry thread, since there are four pairs of strings that have the same length. How much of each color will he need for a class of 24? How much will the string cost?

d. A friend of Stanley's has an extra piece of plywood; it is 6 feet long and 3 1/2 feet wide. If Stanley wants each smaller piece of wood to be big enough so that the nails are 1 inch from the edge of the plywood, will this piece of wood be big enough to make 24 smaller pieces?

e. For a similar project, Stanley needs 684 nails, which come in packages of 18. How many packages will he need?

3. Stanley has decided to have his students make a new string sculpture. He has determined that each group will need exactly 75 inches of string. He has a roll of string that is 912 inches, and he will have 12 pairs of students. Does he have enough string, or will he need to buy more?

4. Patterns in string art sculptures.

a. How many intersection points are there in an 8 by 8 string sculpture?

b. How many intersection points are there in a 20 by 20 string sculpture?

EXPLORATION 3.12   **More Operation Sense: Bidding for a Job**

A big industrial company is preparing for a large meeting. The company has decided to use a contractor to put together the program, stuff and label envelopes, and so on. You are putting together a bid for the job. If you get the bid, the company will give you 2,400 copies of the program, which is 8 pages long. You will need to collate the pages, staple each program, fold the program into an envelope, and place an address sticker on the envelope. If you want to average $8 an hour for this job, how much should you bid?

1. Take some time in your small group to discuss what information you need in order to make the bid and how you will get that information. Once you have a plan, write it down.

2. State your bid and a description of how you obtained the amount. You need to show your instructor how you did each step of the process.

3. What did you learn from doing this exploration?

EXPLORATION 3.13 **Operation Sense in Games**

GAME 1: **Greatest amount**

Materials:

■ One die with the following numbers: 0, 1, 2, 3, 4, 5. (You can simply tape a 0 over the 6 on a standard die.)

Play: Roll the die four times and record the numbers. The object of the game is to place one number in each blank so that the value of the following expression is as great as possible.

$$\square \times \square + \square - \square$$

1. a. Before the first game, stop to think a moment about strategy. Can you describe a master strategy that you think will work for all cases? For example, where will you place the largest number? What if you roll a zero? Write down your master strategy for placing the numbers to make the greatest amount.

   b. Play one round in the following manner. Roll the die four times and record the numbers. Take a moment to think by yourself where you will place the numbers. Go around the group and have each member present a choice and the reasoning behind it. Once you have determined the largest possible value for these four numbers, roll the die four times again and repeat the process. Play as many rounds as you need until each member has found a strategy that that member believes makes sense and will produce the greatest possible number each time.

   c. Write down your master strategy if it has changed from the beginning of the game.

2. The object of the game is to get the greatest amount in the new expression.

$$\square \times \square \div \square + \square$$

   a. Before rolling the die, use your reasoning abilities: Do you think the same master strategy you developed in Step 1 will apply, or do you need to modify it? Write down your thoughts.

   b. Discuss strategies with other members of the group. After the group discussion, if you decide to change your strategy, write down your new strategy.

c. Play several rounds, recording your numbers and your reasoning.

d. Write down your master strategy if it has changed from the beginning of the game.

3. Again, the object of the game is to get the greatest amount.

$$\frac{(\square \times \square)}{(\square - \square)}$$

a. Before rolling the die, use your reasoning abilities: Write your first draft of a master strategy for this expression.

b. Discuss strategies with other members of the group. After the group discussion, if you decide to change your strategy, write down your new strategy.

c. Play several rounds, recording your numbers and your reasoning.

d. Write down your master strategy if it has changed from the beginning of the game.

GAME 2: Smallest amount

1. Now, the object is to make the *smallest* amount.

$$\square \times \square + \square - \square$$

a. Before rolling the die, use your reasoning abilities: Write your first draft of a master strategy for this expression.

b. Discuss strategies with other members of the group. After the group discussion, if you decide to change your strategy, write down your new strategy.

c. Play several rounds, recording your numbers and your reasoning.

d. Write down your master strategy if it has changed from the beginning of the game.

2.   The object is to make the *smallest* amount in the new expression.

$$\square \times \square \div \square + \square$$

   a.   Before rolling the die, use your reasoning abilities: Write your first draft of a master strategy for this expression.

   b.   Discuss strategies with other members of the group. After the group discussion, if you decide to change your strategy, write down your new strategy.

   c.   Play several rounds, recording your numbers and your reasoning.

   d.   Write down your master strategy if it has changed from the beginning of the game.

3.   Again, the object is to make the *smallest* amount.

$$\frac{(\square \times \square)}{(\square - \square)}$$

   a.   Before rolling the die, use your reasoning abilities: Write your first draft of a master strategy for this expression.

   b.   Discuss strategies with other members of the group. After the group discussion, if you decide to change your strategy, write down your new strategy.

   c.   Play several rounds, recording your numbers and your reasoning.

   d.   Write down your master strategy if it has changed from the beginning of the game.

GAME 3: Target

Here is a game that is adapted from the *Fifth-Grade Book* in the NCTM Addenda Series, Grades K–6 (p. 48).

Materials

■ Three dice:
   1, 2, 3, 4, 5, 6
   1, 2, 3, 4, 5, 6
   7, 8, 9, 10, 11, 12

   The object is to get as close to your target number as possible.

Rules

Pick a target number.

Roll the three dice.

Use the three numbers you roll and any combination of operations to get as close as possible to the target number you have chosen.

1.   Let's say the target number was 27 and you rolled 3, 5, 10.

    a. Try on your own to get as close to 27 as you can.

    b. What strategies did you use? Did your understanding of the four operations help you? How?

    c. After you write your responses, discuss your responses with other members of your group.

2.   With your partners, select a target number and roll the dice.

    a. Work by yourself for a few minutes to determine your response.

    b. Compare answers and strategies with other members of your group. If one or more members are closest to the target, discuss strategies. Note any new strategies or methods that you prefer.

    c. Play several more rounds.

Looking Back on Exploration 3.13

In what ways did playing these games help you to learn about how the operations are related?

SECTION 3.3 **EXPLORING MENTAL ARITHMETIC AND ESTIMATION**

Number sense is like common sense with respect to numbers. There is much evidence that suggests that the average American does not have much number sense and that this should concern us. The following explorations present you with opportunities to develop different aspects of number sense.

EXPLORATION 3.14   **How Many . . .? How Far . . .?**

1.   Write down your guess for each of the following numbers. In each case, if there was any reasoning involved (that is, other than a number simply popping into your head), briefly describe the reasoning.

a. What is the population of the city or town in which your college is located?

b. What is the population of the United States?

c. What is the population of the world?

d. What is the number of K−12 schoolchildren in the United States?

e. What is the number of K−12 schoolteachers in the United States?

f. What is the number of doctors in the United States?

g. Decide upon a relatively short distance that all members of the class can relate to—for example, the distance from one spot on campus to another. Decide upon a unit of measurement: feet, miles, minutes. Then estimate the distance.

h. How far is it from New York to Los Angeles?

i. How far is the Earth from the sun?

2. Discuss how you might find answers for each of the questions in Step 1.

3. Under what circumstances does it matter if some (even many) students' guesses are "way off"?

4. Rough guesses.

a. Do you think it is important that people have a rough idea of certain amounts? If you believe it is, explain why. If you believe it is not, explain why not.

b. How rough is rough? For example, what guesses for the population of the United States would be "reasonable"? How did you determine reasonable?

EXPLORATION 3.15 **Mental Arithmetic**

Many of the numbers we see in daily life are estimates, and much of the arithmetic we do involves estimation; for example, recall Exploration 1.3 about how much a new car will cost per year. There are several skills needed for good estimation, one of which is being able to do mental arithmetic—being able to do simple computations in your head rather than doing everything with pencil and paper or with a calculator. The following explorations are designed to develop your mental arithmetic abilities.

PART 1: Mental addition

1.   Do the following ten computations in your head. Briefly note the strategies that you used, and try to give names to them.

One mental tool all students have is being able to visualize the standard algorithm in their heads. For example, for part (a), you could say: "9 + 7 = 16, carry the one, then 5 + 3 = 8 + the carried 1 makes 9; the answer is 96." However, since you already own that method, I ask you not to use it here, but to try others.

a. 39 +57	**b.** 27 +58	**c.** 78 +25	**d.** 46 +19	**e.** 582 +260
f. 625 +147	**g.** 588 +225	**h.** 8,734 + 467	**i.** 645 +547	**j.** 790 +234

Sum	What you did	Name
a.		
b.		
c.		
d.		

Sum	What you did	Name
e.		
f.		
g.		
h.		
i.		
j.		

2. Share your strategies in your small group. Note any strategies that you heard that you did not use but would like to use.

3. In your group, select three or four strategies to describe to the class. Make up a name for each strategy.

4. After hearing the class presentations, write down the strategies that you like best.

PART 2: Mental subtraction

Most people find it more difficult to determine exact answers to subtraction problems in their heads. However, if you think about the various models for subtraction that we have discussed, there are many possibilities: take-away, comparison, adding up, and the fact that the difference between two numbers tells us how far apart they are on the number line, to name but a few.

1.   Do the following computations in your head. Briefly note the strategies that you used other than simply doing the standard algorithm in your head; once again, this strategy is not bad, it's just one that everyone already has. Try to give names to your strategies.

a.	**b.**	**c.**	**d.**	**e.**	**f.**
65	71	80	324	152	1000
−28	−39	−36	−275	− 87	− 378

Difference	What you did	Name
a.		
b.		
c.		
d.		
e.		
f.		

2.   Share your strategies in your small group. Note any strategies that you heard that you did not use but would like to use.

3.   In your group, select three or four strategies to describe to the class. Make up a name for each strategy.

4.   After hearing the class presentations, write down the strategies that you like best.

PART 3: Mental multiplication

1.   Do the following computations in your head. Briefly note the strategies that you used other than simply doing the standard algorithm in your head. Try to give a name to each strategy.

a. 82 × 5	**b.** 24 ×25	**c.** 23 ×12	**d.** 638 × 2	**e.** 70 ×40	**f.** 83 × 24

Product	What you did	Name
a.		
b.		
c.		
d.		
e.		

Product	What you did	Name
f.		

2. Share your strategies in your small group. Note any strategies that you heard that you did not use but would like to use.

3. In your group, select three or four strategies to describe to the class. Make up a name for each strategy.

4. After hearing the class presentations, write down the strategies that you like best.

PART 4: Mental division

1. Do the following computations in your head. Briefly note the strategies that you used, and try to give names to them.

   a. $40\overline{)8,000}$ **b.** $80\overline{)40,000}$ **c.** $72\overline{)3,600}$ **d.** $7\overline{)1,463}$ **e.** $6\overline{)174}$

Quotient	What you did	Name
a.		
b.		
c.		
d.		

Quotient	What you did	Name
e.		

2. Share your strategies in your small group. Note any strategies that you heard that you did not use but would like to use.

3. In your group, select three or four strategies to describe to the class. Make up a name for each strategy.

4. After hearing the class presentations, write down the strategies that you like best.

Looking Back on Exploration 3.15

Are there any strategies that work for more than one operation? Are there any strategies that are similar?

EXPLORATION 3.16 **Having a Party**

Let's say you are having a party and expect 65 people. You want to serve juice. How many bottles of juice should you buy? What additional information do you need to have in order to answer this question? Also, what assumptions or factors will guide your decision? For example, I would assume that the guests will drink more if I serve the juice in large glasses than if I serve it in small glasses. Work on similar preliminary details in Steps 1 and 2 without a calculator.

1. What assumption or factors do you need to agree on before you do any computation?

2. Determine the data that you will need in order to make your estimate. For example, the juice comes in 32-ounce bottles, or 64-ounce bottles, or 1-liter bottles.

3. Now do the actual computation, explaining the steps in your solution.

4. Listen to other groups' presentations.

5. What did you learn from doing this exploration?

EXPLORATION 3.17 **How Much Did They Save?**

Several years ago, the Education Department at Keene State College determined that we could save a substantial amount of money if we purchased a risograph machine (a high-tech mimeograph machine) and used it for duplicating instead of the copying machine. When we use the copying machine, our department is charged 5¢ per copy; with the risograph machine, we are charged 2¢ per copy.

In order to better budget for the future, the department also wanted to get a sense of how much the machine was used, by whom, and how large the runs were. For example, when I duplicate a test for my math class, I make 30 copies. However, when I duplicate an observation form for the 12 sections of the Learning Theory class, I run off 250 copies. The risograph machine has a counter, and professors were asked to record the beginning number, the ending number, the number of copies, the date, and our name. One line in that sheet would look like this:

Date	Begin	End	Number	Professor
9/23	34,567	34,867	300	Bassarear

I took the following data from one week:

- Counter at the beginning of the week: 727,322
- Counter at the end of the week: 740,001
- Total number of runs: 58

I asked myself the following questions, which I would like you to address in the following manner.

1. First, determine your estimate for each of the questions below. (*Note:* An estimate means a number that you can get mentally within a few seconds.) Briefly note what you did in your head. Then go around the group and have each person describe how they obtained an estimate. Describe any strategies that you did not use but that you like.

	Problem	Rough estimate and brief description of how you got it.
a.	What was the total number of copies run that week?	
b.	What was the average number of copies per day?	
c.	What was the average number of copies per run?	

	Problem	Rough estimate and brief description of how you got it.
d.	How much money did we save this week?	

2. Describe any assumptions you are making when you do this problem.

EXPLORATION 3.18 **Making Sense of Little Numbers that Add Up**

1. Let's say someone has a leaky faucet. How much does that drip add up to?

   a. First, discuss and note any assumptions that you will make in doing the problem.

   b. Determine your answer.

2. Environmental scientists need a lot of information to determine how pollution is affecting the environment. For example, trees give off oxygen, and the oxygen given off is proportional to the total area of all the leaves on a tree. Thus, they need to estimate the number of leaves on a tree and the area of an average leaf. Let us tackle a simpler problem here: How many blades of grass do you think there are on an average lawn? Write down your guess.

   a. Let's make the question more focused now. Your class will obtain a piece of sod 1 foot by 1 foot. How many blades of grass do you think there are in this sample? Write your guess and any reasoning that you did.

   b. Share your guess with other members of your group or class. If you wish to change your guess now, do so and briefly explain what ideas caused you to change.

   c. How might you determine the number of blades of grass without counting each one? Write down your ideas and justification.

   d. Share your plans with other members of your group or class. At this point, each group will design and carry out its plan. Describe and justify your plan. Then carry it out; show your work.

e. Each group will present its plan and "answer" to the whole class.

f. If all answers were close, fine. If not, which answer do you feel is closest to the actual amount? Why?

g. What did you learn from doing this exploration?

EXPLORATION 3.19   **Making Sense of Large Numbers**

1. Mars is 34 million miles away. Presently spaceships go about 16,000 miles per hour. How long would it take a spaceship to get to Mars?

2. In 1996 the U.S. federal debt was $4,643,711,000,000. Let's say a decision was made to pay off that debt in much the same way that an individual pays off a debt, such as a car loan or a home mortgage: by paying back a specified amount of money at regular time intervals.

a. Let's say that the decision was made to reduce the debt by $10 million per day. How long would it take to pay off the debt at this rate?

b. Before doing the computations, discuss and note any assumptions that you make.

Number Theory

M any people do not realize that mathematical concepts and ideas often have visual representations. For example, in Chapter 3 you investigated different visual representations of multiplication. In this chapter's explorations, you will be able to visualize some of the concepts that we will study in the text. These explorations can be done with elementary school children, yet they offer interesting challenges to the adult student too.

In each of the following explorations, you will not only lay the foundation for learning some important number theory ideas, but also have the opportunity to develop more mathematical tools—making and testing predictions. Students often tell me that when they think of mathematics, they think of numbers and computations. However, making and testing predictions has been crucial not only to the development of mathematics, but to the development of civilization. Young children are constantly making and testing predictions; I have cleaned up many messes my children made from erroneous predictions! People make and test predictions regularly in both their personal and their professional lives. Yet somehow, this important human activity seems to be absent from much of school mathematics.

SECTION 4.1 **EXPLORING DIVISIBLITY AND RELATED CONCEPTS**

As you discovered in Chapter 3, in order to understand computation algorithms for the four operations and in order to be able to do mental arithmetic and estimation confidently, being able to decompose and recompose a number in different ways is crucial. Depending on the situation, we might decompose 48 as $40 + 8$, as $50 - 2$, as $8 \cdot 6$, or as $2 \cdot 2 \cdot 2 \cdot 2 \cdot 3$. In the following exploration, as you play the Taxman game more times, you will discover that one kind of decomposition of a number will enable you to increase your score, and you will see new relationships among numbers.

EXPLORATION 4.1   **Taxman**

I don't know who invented this game, but I have seen variations in many different places. The version I present to you is one in which a team of two (or more) players competes against the "taxman."

How to play the game:

1.   The team crosses out a number.

2.   The taxman crosses out all the proper factors of that number.

3.   The team crosses out another number. A number can be crossed out only if at least one of its proper factors has not yet been crossed out. For example, you can't cross out 14 if 1, 2, and 7 have all been crossed out already. Play continues until none of the remaining numbers has a proper factor that has not been crossed out.

4.   At the end of the game, the taxman gets all remaining numbers!

5.   To determine your score, add up all the numbers your team crossed out.

1	2	3	4	5	6	7	8	9	10
11	12	13	14	15	16	17	18	19	20

1.   Play several games, using the numbers 1 through 20.

   a.   Record your best game. Briefly justify the choice for each number.

      Number   **Justification**

   b.   Describe and briefly justify any general strategies that you think will be useful when playing the game with bigger numbers.

   c.   After listening to the class discussion, if your game was not the highest scoring one, describe what you learned from the class discussion.

2.   Now play the game with the numbers 1 through 30.

   a.   Record your best game. Briefly justify your choice for each number.

      Number   **Justification**

   b.   Describe and briefly justify any general strategies that you think will be useful when playing the game with bigger numbers.

c. After listening to the class discussion, if your game was not the highest-scoring one, describe what you learned from the class discussion.

3. The following activity is designed to help you develop communication skills and to see the extent to which you can zero in on the most fundamental relationships in the game. Write a set of directions for an imaginary friend Becky, who knows the rules for the game and knows basic mathematics vocabulary, but has never played the game. That is, write a set of directions that are general enough so that she can use them no matter how many numbers she is using.

4. If you were going to play a game from 1 to 100, describe your first three turns and explain your choices.

SECTION 4.2 **EXPLORING PRIME AND COMPOSITE NUMBERS**

A full appreciation of the following explorations requires you to apply ideas of divisibility and enables you to appreciate the relevance of the concept of prime and composite numbers.

EXPLORATION 4.2 **Factors**

An exploration many elementary teachers use to help students develop number sense is to challenge them to make as many different rectangles as they can using a certain number of unit squares. For example, how many different rectangles can be made with six squares?

A lively discussion emerges, and one common debate question is: Are there four different rectangles or two different rectangles? What do you think?

Your answer depends on your definition of *different*. If we define different as how it looks on the page, then we have four different rectangles. If we define different as having a different shape, then we have two different rectangles. This second definition of different is connected to the idea of congruence, which we will study later. In this case, we will use the second definition of different, not because it is "right," but because it connects to some concepts that we will soon develop.

We can make two different rectangles with six unit squares. If we represent them by their length and width, we have a 6×1 rectangle and a 3×2 rectangle. Using mathematical terminology, we can also say that 6 has these four factors: 1, 2, 3, 6.

When elementary school children investigate all the different rectangles they can make for each number, the exploration not only reinforces their multiplication facts, but also addresses other important areas: problem-solving, communication, reasoning, and making connections. Since you are able to think at a more abstract level, we will modify the instructions given to the children.

1. First, list the factors of each of the first 25 natural numbers.

Number	Factors							
1	1							
2	1	2						
3	1	3						
4								
5								
6								
7								
8								
9								
10								
11								
12								
13								
14								
15								
16								
17								
18								
19								
20								
21								
22								
23								
24								
25								

2.   Describe any observations, hypotheses, and questions you have as a result of filling out and looking at the table.

3.   One of the themes of this book is the power of different representations.

    a. Use the data in your table to complete the table below.

1 factor	2 factors	3 factors	4 factors	5 factors	6 factors	7 factors	8 factors
1	2	4					
	3						
	5						

    b. Note any observations, hypotheses, and questions that you have as a result of filling out and looking at this table.

    c. In one sense, the numbers in each column of the table constitute a "family." Can you give a name to any of the families? If so, write down this name (it does not have to be a "mathematical" name) and describe the characteristics that are common to all members of the family.

    d. Suppose we were to continue to look at the factors of numbers beyond 25. Predict (and briefly describe your reasoning) the next number that will have

      ■ 2 factors

      ■ 3 factors

      ■ 4 factors

e. Now extend the table until you have the next number that has 2 factors, 3 factors, and 4 factors. Describe any insights or discoveries from the extension.

f. Can you predict the first number that will have 7 factors? What will it look like? Justify your reasoning.

g. There are other possible families of numbers, based on the number of factors. For example, if we combine the 3-factor families, the 5-factor families, and the 7-factor families into a large family called "odd number of factors," how might you describe the characteristics that are common to all members of *this* family?

EXPLORATION 4.3   **Finding All Factors of a Number**

In this exploration, we will be working with patterns (recognizing, describing, extending), making predictions and hypotheses, and using several related problem-solving tools, including being systematic and making tables.

1. Determine all the factors of 36. Show your work. Describe how confident you are that you have found *all* the factors and why you are very confident, somewhat confident, or not very confident.

2. Select some other numbers and find all of their factors. If you feel that your method is efficient, move on. If you don't feel that your method is very efficient, take some time to stop and think about how else you might determine all the factors of a number.

3. Describe your present method for finding all the factors of a number, as if you were talking to a classmate who missed this exploration.

4. Describe any other observations or hypotheses you have made up to this point.

5. Now compare your methods with those of your partner(s). If you like a method that you heard, summarize this new method in your own words.

6. How could you use the factors of 36 that you found in Step 1 to find all the factors of 72 without starting all over?

7. The number 200 has 12 factors: 1, 2, 4, 5, 8, 10, 20, 25, 40, 50, 100, and 200. This number 200 can be rewritten as $200 = 2^3 \cdot 5^2$. This representation is an example of a *prime factorization,* which is discussed in Section 4.2 of the text. Can you see any way to determine all 12 factors of 200 just from seeing this prime factorization?

SECTION   4.3   **EXPLORING GREATEST COMMON FACTOR AND LEAST COMMON MULTIPLE**

The following explorations, like the previous explorations in this chapter and like many other explorations in this volume, actually involve many concepts. If you did Exploration 4.1 (Taxman), you found that you dealt with divisibility in terms of finding factors of a number, and you found that your strategy for prime numbers was different from your strategy for composite numbers. So too with the star pattern explorations. In fact, you will encounter many number theory concepts in these explorations, and, as with the previous explorations in this chapter, your ability to decompose numbers and then analyze those decompositions and see relationships will enable you to unlock the secrets of star patterns, that is, to understand why they work.

EXPLORATION 4.4   **Star Patterns**

Star patterns have fascinated both mathematicians and students for hundreds of years. They are pleasing to the eye, and they contain many surprises. This exploration extends the work in the exploration with circle clocks in Chapter 3, in which our focus was on multiplication. As you make different star patterns, you will find that exploring relationships among numbers will help you to predict the shape of the figure and the number of paths and orbits needed to make a complete star pattern.

PART 1: Making sense of star patterns

Star patterns are made by beginning at some point on the circle and connecting points at regular intervals. For example, the star on the left below starts at point 0 and jumps to point 2, then point 4, then point 6, and then goes back to 0. The star on the right also begins at point 0, but it jumps three numbers at a time, and so it jumps from 0 to 3 to 6, then (3 points after 6) to 1, 4, and 7, then to 2 and 5, and finally back to 0. Depending on the number of points on the circle and the number of jumps between points, a variety of patterns are created!

1. Take a minute to note what you see and think from these first two star patterns. Note the observations, questions, and hypotheses you have from these two demonstrations. Then share your thoughts with your partner(s). Add or modify any thoughts after the discussion.

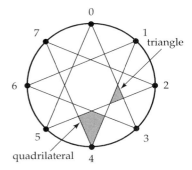

2.   *Patterns in the stars.* The primary focus of this exploration is to examine the relationship between the number of dots we divide the circle into and the way in which we connect the dots. However, before we do that, we will focus on two other aspects of star patterns that uncover important mathematical ideas.

   Let us stop to examine what we see in the stars. For example, look again at the 8-pointed star at the right. This figure has 8 outer vertices, 8 outer figures that are quadrilaterals, and 8 smaller triangles.

   a.   What kind of quadrilateral is made? What kind of triangle is made? If you don't know the names, describe the characteristics of the quadrilateral and the triangle.

   b.   What else do you see?

3.   *Developing a notation.* You have already seen that the mathematical notation that we use was often invented quite recently. You have also seen that these notations are not facts, but rather choices that people made because they thought that the new notations would make it easier to communicate mathematically. Since we will be exploring star patterns, it would be nice to have a simpler way to refer to different star patterns than, for example, "Divide a circle into 8 arcs and then connect every fifth dot." Write down your ideas for ways of representing different star patterns that would be shorter than the present verbal descriptions.

4.   *Initial hypothesis.* We will refer to the star pattern (see page 85) on the left as star $(8, 2)$ and the pattern on the right as star $(8, 3)$. This is a common notation used to describe star patterns and uses the ordered pair idea developed in Chapter 2; that is, the first number tells us how many equal arcs the circle has been divided into, and the second number tells us the rule for connecting dots. However, other notations for naming star patterns are possible, for example, S_2^8 and S_3^8; that is, this way of naming star patterns is a **convention**.

   Now let us focus on the relationships between these two numbers, that is, the number of divisions of the circle and how the points are connected. Looking back to our first two star patterns, which we will now call star patterns $(8, 2)$ and $(8, 3)$, we found that star pattern $(8, 2)$ is a square and star pattern $(8, 3)$ is an eight-pointed star. The question that we will now explore is: Just from looking at the two numbers in any star pattern (x, n), can you predict what the star pattern will look like?

   Brainstorm with your group how you might explore this question. That is, what strategies seem more reasonable or potentially productive? On the following page are several circles that you can trace and then see what patterns emerge when you use different values for x and n. After brainstorming and preliminary exploration, answer the following questions.

a. Describe the strategies that you chose to employ and briefly explain the reasoning for choosing those strategies.

b. Describe your observations, questions, and any preliminary hypotheses from your initial explorations. Explain why you think your hypotheses are true. Note that in mathematics, *true* means true 100 percent of the time. If a hypothesis is true 99 percent of the time, we say that it is false.

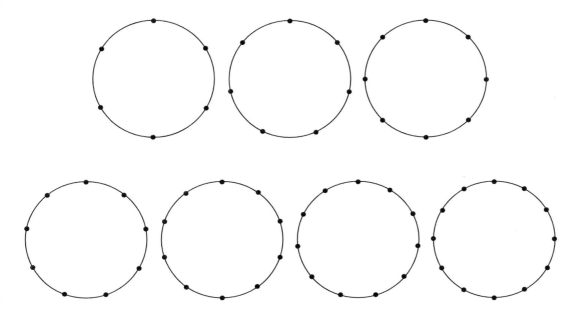

The following activities will help you to generate more data systematically to help you test and refine your hypothesis from Part 1.

PART 2: From observations to hypotheses to generalizations

Exploring One Star Family

In exploring a phenomenon, if often helps to be systematic. This is true not only in mathematics. For example, much medical research involves systematically exploring different combinations of drugs; archaeological work is very systematic; much research in astronomy involves a systematic examination of data.

In this case, we will systematically examine all members of the (8, *n*) star family, that is, all seven star patterns that can be made by dividing a circle into eight arcs.

1. Make the following stars and record your thinking and your work according to the following directions. In each case, first predict (in a chart like the one that follows the diagrams) what you think the star will look like. Afterwards, if your prediction was correct, move on. If it was not, reflect (in the same chart) on what happened, explain why your prediction was not accurate, or explain what you learned in drawing the star.

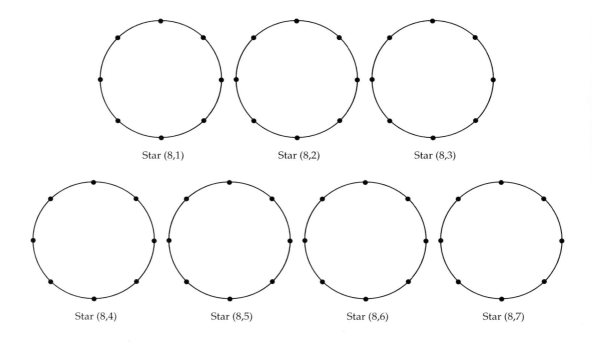

Star (8,1) Star (8,2) Star (8,3)

Star (8,4) Star (8,5) Star (8,6) Star (8,7)

STAR PATTERN (8, 1)

Prediction	
Reflection	

STAR PATTERN (8, 2)

Prediction	
Reflection	

STAR PATTERN (8, 3)

Prediction	
Reflection	

STAR PATTERN (8, 4)

Prediction	
Reflection	

STAR PATTERN (8, 5)

Prediction	
Reflection	

STAR PATTERN (8, 6)

Prediction	
Reflection	

STAR PATTERN (8, 7)

Prediction	
Reflection	

2. After making all of the patterns and filling in the chart, do the following:

   a. Describe any observations that you made and try to explain those observations. For example (8, 3) and (8, 5) are the same. Can you explain why?

   b. State any hypotheses you have about star patterns in general. For example, can you make a prediction about what happens when the second number does or does not divide the first number evenly?

   c. Note any questions that you have.

Exploring Another Star Family

1. Make the following stars. As before, first predict what you think you will find in a chart like the one that follows the diagram, then make the pattern, and then reflect on your prediction (in the chart) if it was not correct.

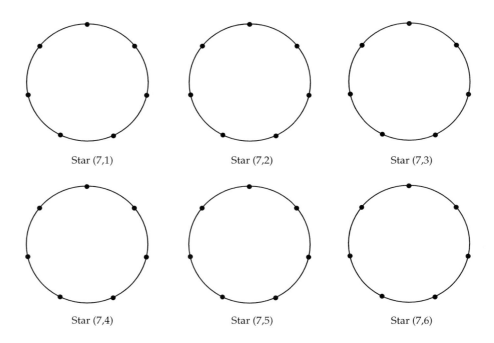

Star (7,1)   Star (7,2)   Star (7,3)

Star (7,4)   Star (7,5)   Star (7,6)

STAR PATTERN (7, 1)

Prediction	
Reflection	

STAR PATTERN (7, 2)

Prediction	
Reflection	

STAR PATTERN (7, 3)

Prediction	
Reflection	

STAR PATTERN (7, 4)

Prediction	
Reflection	

STAR PATTERN (7, 5)

Prediction	
Reflection	

STAR PATTERN (7, 6)

Prediction	
Reflection	

2. After making all the patterns and filling in the chart, do the following:

   a. Describe any observations that you made and try to explain those observations.

   b. State any hypotheses you have about star patterns in general.

   c. Note any questions that you have.

Gathering More Data

In its most open-ended form, the task of this exploration is to note what you observe about star patterns in order to predict a star's appearance simply from knowing the number of points on the star and the number of jumps. That is, for star (x, n), if you are given the values of x and n, can you predict what it will look like?

1. Because so many students are so new to this idea of looking for patterns and making and testing predictions, the directions here will not be quite so open-ended. Therefore, make other star families on your own—for example, circles with 6 dots, 9 dots, 10 dots, and so forth (see pages 95 and 96). As you do so, look for patterns. For example, depending on the x and n, some stars will look like geometric figures (triangles, squares, and so forth), and some stars will look very similar to other stars.

2. When making star patterns of the form $(8, n)$ and $(7, n)$, you found that some of the stars were equal; for example, star $(8, 3)$ = star $(8, 5)$. Can you jump from this observation to a more general hypothesis? For example, when will $(x, a) = (x, b)$?

3. Some of you may have realized that there are other instances in which two star patterns will be equal. For example, draw the $(12, n)$ star family and the $(6, n)$ family if you have not yet done so. Is it possible that there are numbers a and b such that star $(12, a)$ = star $(6, b)$? Can you state your observations as one or more hypotheses?

4. What other hypotheses have you come up with? State your hypotheses and explain why you think they are true.

5. The following questions that are often raised by students deal with the ideas of limitations on x and n. Answer these questions.

   a. Is it possible to have star (x, x)? If so, what would it look like? If not, why not?

   b. Is it possible to have star $(x, 0)$? If so, what would it look like? If not, why not?

   c. Is it possible to have star $(x, {}^-1)$? If so, what would it look like? If not, why not?

EXPLORATION 4.5   Paths and Orbits in Star Patterns

We have found that when we make star patterns, sometimes we will connect all the points on the circle without lifting our pen or pencil and sometimes we will not. From one perspective, if not all the points have been used, the star is incomplete. For example, the figure on the left below shows star $(8, 2)$, which is not complete. However, if we move over one point (to point 1) and connect every other dot, we now have a "complete" star, as shown on the right.

Star pattern (8,2)

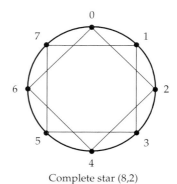

Complete star (8,2)

Paths

To use language that other mathematicians have used, we can say that to complete star $(8, 2)$, we have to make two **paths.** A path can be defined as the figure made by starting at one point and continuing until you reach that point again. Thus, the complete star $(8, 2)$ consists of 2 paths.

1. Can you predict the number of paths it will take to make a complete star? That is, how many paths does star (x, n) have?

    Suggestion: Make some stars with different x's and different n's. Note the number of paths it takes to make a complete star. Do this until you feel that you can predict the number of paths in the complete star knowing only x and n. Note that there are *universal hypotheses,* those that will work for all x's and n's, and there are *specific hypotheses* (an example of a specific hypothesis is, "All stars of the form $(7, n)$ will have exactly 1 path").

2. If a star has more than one path, must each path in that star be the same length? What do you think?

3. If a star has more than one path, must each path in that star contain the same number of points? What do you think? Is this question essentially the same as the one asked in Step 2? Why or why not?

Orbits

We can also speak of the number of *orbits* in a star pattern.

4. Before we begin, what do you think an orbit will mean? For example, look back to your previous work. How many orbits are there in star $(8, 2)$? in star $(7, 2)$? Do this before reading on.

    One simple definition of **orbit** is a trip around the circle in which you either "pass" your starting point or land "at" your starting point. Thus star $(8, 2)$ has one orbit because when you end up at the starting point, you have gone around the circle once. However, star $(7, 2)$ has 2 orbits because you must go around the circle 2 times before you arrive at the original starting point. The figures below demonstrates this fact. If we designate 0 as the starting point, our path goes from 0 to 2 to 4 to 6 to 1. At this point, we have gone around the circle once (actually slightly more than once). If we continue, we go from 1 to 3 to 5 to 0. We now have gone around the circle twice and have arrived at our starting point. Therefore, star $(7, 2)$ has 2 orbits.

Star Pattern (7,2)

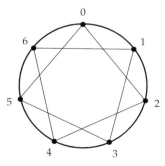

5. Can you predict the number of orbits in a star pattern? That is, how many orbits will star (x, n) have?

Suggestion: Make a number of star patterns with different x's and n's. Note the number of orbits in each star. Do this until you feel you can predict the number of orbits in any star knowing only x and n.

Looking Back

1. One of the objectives of the star explorations was to introduce several number theory ideas.

    a. Write your definition of one or two number theory concepts that evolved from these explorations, for example, factor, multiple, prime, and relatively prime.

    b. Exchange definitions with a partner. Critique your partner's definition with respect to accuracy and then with respect to clarity. That is, you may feel that it is not accurate. For example, if someone says that x is a *multiple* of y if you can multiply x by a number to get y, this is not accurate. Such a description has confused *multiple* with *factor*. On the other hand, to say that x is a multiple of y if you can multiply y by a number to get x is also not accurate because we really need to say *whole number*: "x is a multiple of y if you can multiply y by a whole number to get x."

    c. After you receive the critique of your definitions from your partner, write second drafts of your definitions. That is, each of your definitions should have the following: "draft," "critique," and "second draft."

    Draft:

    Critique:

    Second draft:

2. Another main objective of these explorations is to help you learn to "see" more patterns, learn how to turn observed patterns into questions and hypotheses, and then learn how to test those hypotheses to determine whether they are true (in which case they become theorems) or false. This process actually breaks into three interconnected but distinguishable parts.

    a. Do you feel that you have learned to see more patterns? Describe, as if you were talking to a student who missed this exploration, what advice you would give to help that person see more patterns.

    b. Describe, as if you were talking to a student who missed this exploration, what advice you would give to help that person move from just seeing more patterns to converting those observations into hypotheses. If, for example, you say "be systematic," describe what being systematic means to you.

c. Describe, as if you were talking to a student who missed this exploration, what advice you would give to help that person test hypotheses to determine whether they are true or false. It is worth repeating that although famous mathematicians are famous for their correct hypotheses, all the mathematicians that I know readily admit that they have had many hypotheses turn out to be false also.

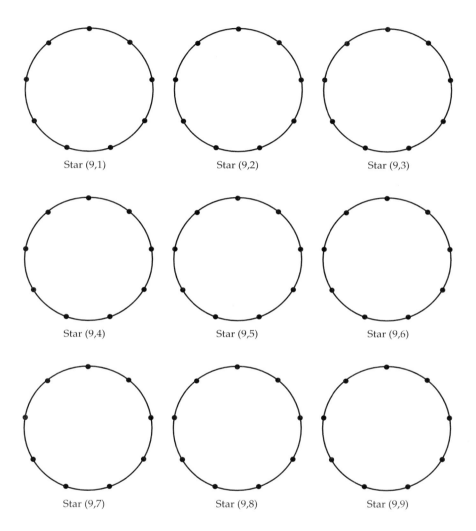

Star (9,1) Star (9,2) Star (9,3)

Star (9,4) Star (9,5) Star (9,6)

Star (9,7) Star (9,8) Star (9,9)

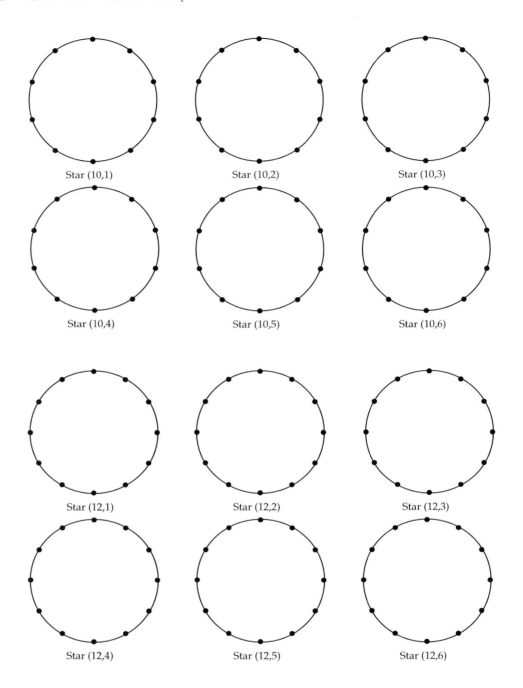

Star (10,1)　　　Star (10,2)　　　Star (10,3)

Star (10,4)　　　Star (10,5)　　　Star (10,6)

Star (12,1)　　　Star (12,2)　　　Star (12,3)

Star (12,4)　　　Star (12,5)　　　Star (12,6)

Extending the Number System

Many beginning elementary teachers think that they will never have to teach fractions, integers, or decimals unless they teach upper elementary school. While this may have been true in the past, it is not true anymore. Even in kindergarten, children encounter the idea of fractions in terms of dividing: We each get half. Second graders will often ask, "Why can't you take 8 from 2?" when a teacher introduces regrouping (for example, $52 - 38$). Long before formal work with decimal operations, children encounter decimals when they deal with money. Therefore, it is essential that all elementary teachers have an understanding of the relationship of these three systems (integers, fractions, and decimals) to whole numbers and to each other.

SECTION 5.1 **EXPLORING INTEGERS**

Although most students do not encounter integers until middle school, many elementary school children are aware of them, and quite a few will be able to work with them. Therefore, it is important that the elementary teacher be comfortable with integers from a conceptual point of view — that is, how they connect to positive whole numbers and how operations with integers are like and unlike operations with positive whole numbers. The following explorations are designed to help you better understand integer operations.

EXPLORATION 5.1 **Understanding Integer Addition**

When we examined addition with positive whole numbers, one model we used to represent this operation was the set (discrete) model. Let us use this model to develop rules for integer addition. We will use black dots to represent positive numbers and white dots to represent negative numbers.[1] Thus, the figure below is a representation of 3 + 4 in the context of addition as joining. That is, we have two sets, one containing 3 dots and the other containing 4 dots. When we combine the two sets, we have 7 dots; that is, 3 + 4 = 7.

1.   Model the problem 5 + ⁻2. Describe and justify your process so that a reader who is not familiar with integer addition could understand both how you got the answer and why your process works.

2.   Model the problem ⁻7 + 5. Describe and justify your process so that a reader who is not familiar with integer addition could understand both how you got the answer and why your process works.

3.   Model the problem ⁻3 + ⁻6. Describe and justify your process so that a reader who is not familiar with integer addition could understand both how you got the answer and why your process works.

4.   We have now examined all four cases that can occur when adding integers: both numbers positive, the larger magnitude positive, the larger magnitude negative, and both numbers negative. Based on your work above, can you describe a general rule for adding integers that will work for all cases?

EXPLORATION 5.2   **Understanding Integer Subtraction**

As you discovered in Chapter 3, different contexts for subtraction lead to very different diagrams. We will examine integer subtraction first in the take-away context and then in the comparison context.

Subtraction as Take-Away

On the top of page 99 is a representation of 5 − 2 from the take-away perspective. That is, the figure at the left shows 5 objects. The figure at the right shows us taking 2 away, and thus 3 objects remain; that is, 5 − 2 = 3.

---

[1] In many elementary classrooms, teachers will use black checkers to represent positive numbers and red checkers to represent negative numbers.

1.   Model the problem $2 - 5$; that is, 2 take away 5.

2.   Describe and justify your process so that a reader who is not familiar with integer subtraction could understand both how you got the answer and why your process works.

3.   Many students struggle to find a way to model this problem. As with all mathematics, someone, somewhere, sometime, was able to come up with a model that was useful. The key to the following model is to use the idea of *additive inverses:* For any number a, there is a number ^-a (the additive inverse) such that $a + {}^-a = 0$.

The circle to the right represents the first step in the problem $2 - 5$. Do you see why? Work on this before reading on. . . .

The overall value of the objects in this circle is still $^+2$. Now we can apply our take-away model of subtraction. We can "take away" 5; that is, we take away 5 black circles. Thus, we have demonstrated with the chips that $2 - 5 = {}^-3$, because the value of what is left is $^-3$.

4.   Model the problem $^-3 - 6$. Describe and justify your process so that a reader who is not familiar with integer subtraction could understand both how you got the answer and why your process works.

5.   Model the problem $4 - {}^-5$. Describe and justify your process so that a reader who is not familiar with integer subtraction could understand both how you got the answer and why your process works.

6.   Model the problem $^-2 - {}^-4$. Describe and justify your process so that a reader who is not familiar with integer subtraction could understand both how you got the answer and why your process works.

7.   We have now examined all four cases that can occur when subtracting integers. Based on your work above, can you describe a general rule for subtracting integers that will work for subtraction as take away?

Subtraction as Comparison

As you saw in Chapter 3, and as most first and second graders will readily tell you, subtraction as comparison is quite different from subtraction as take-away. The key to being able to model integer subtraction resulting from the subtraction as comparison context is to find a way to adapt our notion of subtraction as comparison so that it works with integers. For example, we could describe $6 - 2$ as comparison by saying that this means "How much bigger is 6 than 2?" See the figure at the right. We can readily see that 6 is 4 bigger than 2. However, this way of describing subtraction as comparison doesn't help us with problems like $^-3 - 6$, because we would ask, "How much bigger is $^-3$ than 6?"

8.   Work with your partners to find a way to describe subtraction as comparison that will work for the cases we examined with take-away, that is, $2 - 5$, $^-3 - 6$, $4 - ^-5$, and $^-2 - ^-4$.

   a.   Model the problem $2 - 5$. Describe and justify your process so that a reader who is not familiar with integer subtraction could understand both how you got the answer in the context of subtraction as comparison and why your process works.

   b.   Model the problem $^-3 - 6$. Describe and justify your process so that a reader who is not familiar with integer subtraction could understand both how you got the answer in the context of subtraction as comparison and why your process works.

   c.   Model the problem $4 - ^-5$. Describe and justify your process so that a reader who is not familiar with integer subtraction could understand both how you got the answer in the context of subtraction as comparison and why your process works.

   d.   Model the problem $^-2 - ^-4$. Describe and justify your process so that a reader who is not familiar with integer subtraction could understand both how you got the answer in the context of subtraction as comparison and why your process works.

9.   We have now examined all four cases that can occur when subtracting integers. Based on your work above, can you describe a general rule for subtracting that will work for subtraction as comparison?

Looking Back

Based on your work above, can you describe and justify a general rule or set of rules for *any* subtraction problem?

E X P L O R A T I O N 5.3   **Understanding Integer Multiplication**

Below is a representation of 4 · 3 using chips. It uses the repeated addition context for multiplication. That is, we have four sets of 3, or three 4 times.

1.   What about 4 · ⁻3?

   a.   Model and solve this problem by using or adapting the idea of multiplication as repeated addition.

   b.   Describe and justify your process so that a reader who is not familiar with integer multiplication could understand both how you got the answer and why your process works.

2.   What about ⁻4 · 3?

   a.   Model and solve this problem by using or adapting the idea of multiplication as repeated addition.

   b.   Describe and justify your process so that a reader who is not familiar with integer multiplication could understand both how you got the answer and why your process works.

3.   Model the problem ⁻4 · ⁻3. Describe and justify your process so that a reader who is not familiar with integer multiplication could understand both how you got the answer and why your process works.

4.   We have now examined all four cases that can occur when multiplying integers. Based on your work above, can you describe a general rule for multiplying integers.

E X P L O R A T I O N 5.4   **Understanding Integer Division**

Repeated Subtraction and Partitioning Models

Consider the problem 8 ÷ 2. We learned in Chapter 3 that we can represent this problem using the partitioning model of division, and we can represent this problem using the repeated subtraction **model** of division. For review, you may want to model the problem 8 ÷ 2 with the partitioning model and with the repeated subtraction model.

1. **a.** Model the problem ⁻8 ÷ 2 with the partitioning model.

    b. Model the same problem with the repeated subtraction model.

    c. Describe and justify your process so that a reader who is not familiar with integer division could understand both how you got the answer and why your process works.

Missing Factor Model

When we get to other cases of integer division (for example, 8 ÷ ⁻2 and ⁻8 ÷ ⁻2), these two models become more and more complex, and at some point, they pass into the realm of "more trouble than it's worth." Therefore, let us abandon the partitioning and repeated subtraction models for division and look to another model for division to justify the procedures for integer division, the missing factor model—that is, the solution to $a \div b$ can be found by asking, "What number times b is equal to a?"

2. Use the missing factor model to determine the answers to the following three problems. As before, describe and justify your process so that a reader who is not familiar with integer division could understand both how you got the answer and why your process works.

$$^-8 \div 2$$
$$12 \div {}^-3$$
$$^-20 \div {}^-4$$

3. We have now examined all four cases that can occur when dividing integers. Based on your work above, can you describe a general rule for dividing integers?

SECTION   5.2   **EXPLORING FRACTIONS AND RATIONAL NUMBERS**

Researchers have told us for years that students' understanding of rational numbers is poor. This is unfortunate because the concept of rational numbers is one of the big ideas in elementary school mathematics. The fraction explorations here have been designed to have you work with the fundamental concepts related to fractions. Just as we discussed different decompositions of whole numbers in Chapters 3 and 4, a key to understanding fractions is to decompose them. That is, the notion of parts and wholes connects to our compositions and decompositions with whole numbers. We shall investigate various decompositions, which in turn will deepen your understanding of the different fraction contexts and the relationship between the numerator and the denominator.

    As you found with whole numbers, one can be able to compute but not understand the operations and procedures. As you develop your understanding of the many ways in which fractions can be interpreted and how these interpretations connect to the meanings of addition, subtraction, multiplication, and division, you will be able to work with fractions confidently and powerfully — that is, you will be able to solve multistep and nonroutine problems.

EXPLORATION 5.5   **Making Manipulatives**

Using manipulatives in elementary school mathematics was one of the bandwagons of the 1980s. In fact, "hands-on" became one of those infamous buzzwords. However, hands-on alone is not enough. One modification of this phrase is "hands-on and minds-on." In other words, although manipulatives help to ground one's understanding of new ideas, what the hands do needs to be connected to important ideas in the mathematical concept.

One of the reasons for the limited success of much work with manipulatives on fractions is that even when students have worked with manipulatives, they have often worked with premade manipulatives. Although there is a place for premade manipulatives in the curriculum, many mathematics educators believe that at some point early in their development, students will benefit tremendously by making their own manipulatives. Such an activity not only allows the students to grapple with concepts at a deeper level, but also invites more creativity on their part. The following exploration has been one of my students' favorites.

Making the Manipulatives

1. Make a set of fraction manipulatives. Some of you will make fraction manipulatives from circles and some from squares. Regardless of which manipulatives you make, read the questions in Steps 2 to 6 below and keep them in mind as you make your manipulatives.

    Circles: Using construction paper that has been cut into circles of the same size, make a set of manipulatives. The only restriction is that you cannot use a protractor. For example, you cannot make 1/4 circles by measuring 90-degree angles. In addition to physical tools, you will also need to use a combination of problem-solving strategies, including reasoning and guess–check–revise.

    Squares: Using construction paper that has been cut into squares of the same size, make a set of manipulatives. The only restriction is that you cannot use a ruler to measure the divisions, although you can use a ruler to draw straight lines. For example, if your square is 6 inches on a side, you cannot use the ruler to make a mark every 2 inches. In addition to physical tools, you will also need to use a combination of problem-solving strategies, including reasoning and guess–test–revise.

    After you have made your manipulatives, respond to the following questions.

2. Describe at least two general strategies that you used when making the manipulatives — that is, strategies that you used for more than just one or two denominators.

3. **a.** Describe how you made thirds as if you were talking to someone who missed class. Your description needs to have enough specificity so that the person could repeat what you did and see why you did it that way.

    b. Describe how you made fifths as if you were talking to someone who missed class.

4. How did you check to see if each fraction in a set was the same size before you cut? You may describe a general rule or explain what you did for a specific denominator.

5. Describe at least two learnings that resulted from making your set of manipulatives. These may be framed as statements or hypotheses.

6. Describe any questions that you have at this point, either questions about how to make a particular fraction (such as ninths) or other questions that arose when you were making your sets.

7. Discuss your responses with your partner(s). Make any changes in your answers as a result of the discussion.

Extensions

8. Imagine explaining fractions to an Alphabitian.

    a. How would you define the term *fraction* in your own words?

    b. How would you define the term *numerator* in your own words?

    c. How would you define the term *denominator* in your own words?

9. Alicia said that making 1/5 was hard. Brandon said that it was easy because 1/5 is "halfway between 1/4 and 1/6." What do you think? Jamie said that Brandon's method can be used for lots of cases; for example, 1/7 will be halfway between 1/6 and 1/8; 1/6 will be halfway between 1/4 and 1/8.

    a. What is your initial reaction to Brandon's statement? Do you feel that 1/5 is halfway between 1/4 and 1/6 or not? Why?

    b. Discuss this question in your group. If you changed your mind, explain what changed your mind and justify your present position. If you didn't change your mind, but you feel you can better justify your response, write your revised justification below.

10. Leah called some fractions "prime fractions." What do you think she meant?

Looking Back on Exploration 5.5

Describe your most important learning(s) from this exploration.

EXPLORATION 5.6 **Ordering Fractions[2]**

With the widespread use of calculators and the increasing use of the metric system, the use of fractions in computation in everyday life has diminished considerably. However, understanding fraction relationships is still important because of the connection between fractions and ratios and the connection between fractions and decimals. Understanding these fraction relationships is an important underpinning of what we call *proportional reasoning*.

  In this exploration, you will be asked to use your knowledge of fractions and your reasoning to order fractions. We will ask you to do this without finding the LCM or using a calculator to convert them to decimals. That would be appropriate if the goal were simply to have you be able to do the conversion. Similarly, you are encouraged to use the manipulatives you made in Exploration 5.5 to help you answer the questions, but the justification needs to go beyond the manipulatives to connect to fraction ideas. For example, 5/9 is greater than 4/9 because both fractions have the same denominator, and hence each of the pieces is the same size. Therefore, having 5 such pieces is more than having 4 such pieces. As you grapple with determining which fraction in each pair is greater, see what connections you can make to your understanding of "fraction," "numerator," and "denominator."

Directions:

Work in a group.
  For each of the pairs of fractions below:

1. Predict the relative values by inserting the symbol $<$, $=$, or $>$ into the space between the fractions, and briefly justify your reasoning.

	Fraction	>, =, or <	Fraction	Justification
a.	$\dfrac{3}{5}$		$\dfrac{3}{8}$	
b.	$\dfrac{5}{6}$		$\dfrac{7}{8}$	
c.	$\dfrac{3}{5}$		$\dfrac{5}{12}$	
d.	$\dfrac{1}{2}$		$\dfrac{17}{31}$	

[2] This exploration has been adapted from one developed by the Summermath for Teachers program at Mt. Holyoke College and the Mathematics for Tomorrow project at Education Development Center.

	Fraction	>, =, or <	Fraction	Justification
e.	$\dfrac{3}{8}$		$\dfrac{2}{9}$	
f.	$\dfrac{9}{12}$		$\dfrac{6}{8}$	
g.	$\dfrac{1}{4}$		$\dfrac{2}{9}$	
h.	$\dfrac{9}{11}$		$\dfrac{7}{9}$	
i.	$\dfrac{13}{25}$		$\dfrac{5}{8}$	
j.	$\dfrac{3}{10}$		$\dfrac{9}{23}$	

2. Check your responses with your partner(s). In some cases you may have the same answer but different justifications. Listen to one another; remember that just because you have the right answer does not mean your reasoning is valid. By the same token, a wrong answer often contains some valid reasoning. On some questions, you may disagree. Listen to one another; see if you can find the misconception(s) in someone's reasoning.

3. After the group discussion, take some time to write what you learned from the discussion.

4. With your partner(s), develop a set of general rules that could be used by another person. There are many possible rules and ways to state them. For example, if two fractions have the same denominator, the fraction with the larger numerator is greater. Justify at least two of your rules; that is, explain *why* they work.

5. Exchange rules with another group. Then order the following fractions *using the other group s rules*.

	Fraction	>, =, or <	Fraction	Justification
a.	$\dfrac{3}{4}$		$\dfrac{7}{12}$	
b.	$\dfrac{5}{8}$		$\dfrac{10}{13}$	
c.	$\dfrac{5}{12}$		$\dfrac{7}{13}$	

	Fraction	>, =, or <	Fraction	Justification
d.	$\dfrac{7}{10}$		$\dfrac{14}{19}$	
e.	$\dfrac{2}{7}$		$\dfrac{1}{3}$	
f.	$\dfrac{3}{8}$		$\dfrac{4}{7}$	

6. Critique the other group's rules with respect first to validity and then clarity. That is, if you feel that any of the rules are invalid, explain why. If you feel that any rules are not clear, circle the words or phrases that are ambiguous or unclear and explain why you find them ambiguous or unclear.

7. Based on the critique from the other group, make any necessary changes in your rules.

8. What if we introduce *improper fractions* into the question? Either create new rules to determine the relative value of the fractions below or adapt old rules so they will work for improper fractions.

a.	$\dfrac{4}{3}$		$\dfrac{9}{8}$	
b.	$\dfrac{19}{7}$		$\dfrac{39}{12}$	

9. Order each set of fractions. Explain your thinking process.

a. $\dfrac{31}{80} \quad \dfrac{13}{17} \quad \dfrac{2}{3}$

b. $\dfrac{1}{3} \quad \dfrac{4}{7} \quad \dfrac{5}{8} \quad \dfrac{6}{13} \quad \dfrac{5}{14}$

c. $\dfrac{1}{3} \quad \dfrac{4}{7} \quad \dfrac{2}{5} \quad \dfrac{7}{8} \quad \dfrac{5}{16}$

d. $\dfrac{3}{10} \quad \dfrac{2}{3} \quad \dfrac{7}{12} \quad \dfrac{4}{5} \quad \dfrac{3}{7}$

e. $\dfrac{1}{8} \quad \dfrac{2}{5} \quad \dfrac{5}{8} \quad \dfrac{5}{6} \quad \dfrac{3}{49} \quad \dfrac{3}{56}$

Looking Back on Exploration 5.6

Describe your most important learning(s) from this exploration.

EXPLORATION 5.7   **Partitioning Wholes**

Let us briefly discuss the idea of multiple representations, which has become a cornerstone teaching principle for most mathematics educators and is derived from the work of Jerome Bruner and Zoltan Dienes. As we have discovered in Chapter 3, each of the four operations can be represented in different ways. With respect to fractions, it is crucial that you work with different representations. First, many mathematics educators have emphasized that students will construct much more powerful understandings of a concept if they explore that concept in a variety of physical contexts. Second, one representation is often more appropriate than others for a problem situation.

There are many different ways in which we can represent fractions; in this text, we will focus on area models, discrete models, and number line models. Physical representations include circles, rectangles, Pattern Blocks, and Geoboards for the area model; Cuisenaire rods and fraction bars for the number line model; and small circles for the discrete model. After a concept is introduced with one manipulative, many researchers recommend presenting the learner with a different manipulative; this will cause the learner to rethink the concept because most physical representations have different perceptual features that highlight some aspects of the concept(s) and do not address other aspects.[3]

FRACTION MODELS

Area Models		Discrete Models	Number Line Models
circles	◐ ◯		
squares and rectangles	▦ ☐ ▭	small circles ◯◯◯◯◯	Cuisenaire rods
pattern blocks	⬡ ▽ ▱ △		number line 0 10 20 30 40
geoboards	◰		

Part 1: Understanding area models

In each of the steps below, you will be asked to do the problems yourself and then discuss your solution(s) with your partner(s). If you decide that some of your solutions were not correct, do not erase them. Describe your mistake, redo the problem, and justify your new solution.

1.   Suppose each of the rectangles below has the value of 1. Divide each rectangle into the number of equal pieces called for. Justify your solutions.

     a. 2 equal pieces   2 equal pieces

[3] Douglas T. Owens, ed., *Middle Grades Mathematics* (Reston, Va.: National Council of Teachers of Mathematics, 1993), p. 122.

b. 3 equal pieces [   ]   3 equal pieces [   ]

c. 8 equal pieces [   ]   8 equal pieces [   ]

d. After the discussion with your partner(s), note important things that you learned from wrong answers, from different answers, or from correct answers. Try to connect these reflections to fraction ideas — for example, "I always thought two pieces had to be the same shape; now I realize that two parts can be 1/4 but not look the same."

2. Suppose each of the triangles below has the value of 1. Divide each triangle into the number of equal pieces called for. Justify your solutions.

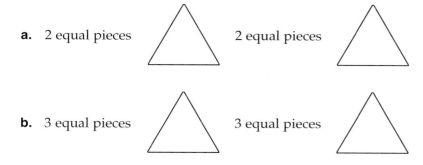

a. 2 equal pieces   2 equal pieces

b. 3 equal pieces   3 equal pieces

c. After the discussion with your partner(s), note important things that you learned from wrong answers, from different answers, or from correct answers. Try to connect these reflections to fraction ideas.

3. Draw a diagram that has the specified value. Again, a primary purpose of these questions is to focus on the meaning of the numerator and denominator and their relationship. Justify your solutions.

a. If [   ] $= \dfrac{1}{3}$, show 1.

b. If [   ] $= \dfrac{3}{4}$, show 1.

c. If [   ] $= 1\dfrac{1}{3}$, show 1.

d. After the discussion with your partner(s), note important things that you learned from wrong answers, from different answers, or from correct answers. Try to connect these reflections to fraction ideas.

4. The following questions relate to Pattern Blocks, a manipulative commonly found in elementary school classrooms. Justify your solutions.

a. If ⬡ $= \frac{2}{3}$, show 1.

b. If ⬠ $= \frac{3}{4}$, show 1.

c. If ⬡⬡ $= \frac{4}{3}$, show 1.

d. If ⬡⬡ $= 1$, show $\frac{1}{8}$.

e. If ⬠ $= \frac{3}{4}$, what is the value of ▱?

f. After the discussion with your partner(s), note important things that you learned from wrong answers, from different answers, or from correct answers. Try to connect these reflections to fraction ideas.

5. a. If the whole region has a value of 1, what is the approximate value of the shaded region? Explain your reasoning.

b. If the large square has a value of 1, then determine the approximate value of the small square. Explain your reasoning.

c. If each of the hexagons below has a value of 1, does each individual piece in each of the hexagons represent 1/6? Why or why not?

d. Are either or both of the following figures below valid representations of 4/3? Why or why not?

e. After the discussion with your partner(s), note important things that you learned from wrong answers, from different answers, or from correct answers. Try to connect these reflections to fraction ideas.

Part 2: Understanding discrete models

1. **a.** If $\begin{smallmatrix}\bullet&\bullet&\bullet\\\bullet&\bullet&\end{smallmatrix}$ $= \dfrac{2}{3}$, show 1.

   b. If $\begin{smallmatrix}\bullet&\bullet\\\bullet&\bullet&\bullet\\\bullet&\bullet\end{smallmatrix}$ $= 1$, show $\dfrac{3}{4}$.

   c. If $\begin{smallmatrix}\bullet&\bullet&\bullet&\bullet\\\bullet&\bullet&\bullet&\bullet\\\bullet&\bullet&\bullet&\bullet\end{smallmatrix}$ $= 2\dfrac{2}{3}$, show 1.

   d. If $\begin{smallmatrix}\bullet&\bullet\\\bullet&\bullet&\bullet\end{smallmatrix}$ $= \dfrac{1}{3}$, show $\dfrac{1}{2}$.

2. What fraction of the circles are black? Your answer needs to have a denominator other than 12, and you need to be able to justify your answer.

3. After the discussion with your partner(s), note important things that you learned from wrong answers, from different answers, or from correct answers. Try to connect these reflections to fraction ideas.

Part 3: Understanding number line models

1. **a.** On the number line below, mark the approximate location of 1. Explain your reasoning.

   b. On the number line below, mark the approximate location of 1. Explain your reasoning.

   c. On the number line below, approximate the value of x. Explain your reasoning.

d. On the number line below, approximate the value of *x*. Explain your reasoning.

e. After the discussion with your partner(s), note important things that you learned from wrong answers, from different answers, or from correct answers. Try to connect these reflections to fraction ideas.

Looking Back on Exploration 5.7

1. Which models were easier for you to work with? Why?

2. Which models were harder for you to work with? Why?

3. Describe your most important learnings.

4. Describe any problems that still puzzle you.

EXPLORATION 5.8   **Developing Fraction Sense**

After each part, compare your responses and your justification with your partner(s). As before, if you agree, listen to one another's justifications. If you disagree, discuss and debate until you reach agreement.

Part 1: Naming Fractions[4]

For each step below, (a) give your answer, (b) explain your thinking (that is, how did you come up with your answer?), and (c) justify your response (that is, why do you believe it is correct?).

1. Name a fraction between 1/6 and 2/6.

2. Name a fraction between 9/10 and 1.

3. Name a fraction that is very close to 1. Now name a fraction that is even closer to 1.

---

[4] Adopted from Activity 16 in Barbara Reyes, et al., *Developing Number Sense in the Middle Grades, Addenda Series, Grades 5–8* (Reston, Va.: NCTM, 1991).

4.   Name a fraction that is greater than 1/2 but closer to 1/2 than to 5/8.

5.   Give a value of x that makes the following statement true: $0 < \dfrac{4}{x} < \dfrac{1}{10}$.

6.   Name a fraction between 0 and 1/10 that does not have a numerator of 1.

7.   **a.**   Make a number line and represent 1/2, 2/3, and 3/4 as closely as you can to their "exact" location. Describe your reasoning.

      b.   Is 2/3 closer to 3/4 or to 1/2? Can you justify your answer by a means other than "it looks closer to x"?

8.   After the discussion with your partner(s), note important things that you learned from wrong answers, from different answers, or from correct answers. Try to connect these reflections to fraction ideas.

Part 2: Fraction benchmarks[5]

1.   **a.**   Place each of the fractions below in one of three groups: closer to 0, closer to 1/2, or closer to 1.

$$\frac{3}{8} \quad \frac{2}{7} \quad \frac{1}{3} \quad \frac{21}{50} \quad \frac{4}{5} \quad \frac{7}{11} \quad \frac{31}{181}$$

Closer to 0	Closer to 1/2	Closer to 1

      b.   Briefly justify each choice.

      c.   Compare your responses and your justification with your partner(s). As before, if you agree, listen to one another's justifications. If you disagree, discuss and debate until you reach agreement.

      d.   Describe any important learnings about fractions as a result of the discussion.

2.   **a.**   Describe a general rule for deciding whether a fraction is closer to 0 or to 1/2.

---

[5] Adapted from Activity 18 in Reyes et al., *Developing Number Sense in the Middle Grades.*

b.   Describe a general rule for deciding whether a fraction is closer to 1/2 or to 1.

3.   After the discussion with your partner(s), note important things that you learned from wrong answers, from different answers, or from correct answers. Try to connect these reflections to fraction ideas.

S E C T I O N   ◆ 5.3 ◆   **EXPLORING OPERATIONS WITH FRACTIONS**

As you may have already known before this course, being able to perform fraction computations and being able to apply fraction knowledge in real-life problems are not the same thing. As in Chapter 3, understanding the whys behind the whats is crucial if you are going to be an effective teacher of children. If you do the explorations in this section conscientiously, you will come out with a much stronger "fraction sense" and you will better understand why the various fraction algorithms actually work!

E X P L O R A T I O N 5.9   **Developing Operation Sense**

This exploration focuses on further refining your operation sense, which we first explored in Chapter 3. This involves developing the ability to compute mentally with fractions and developing operation sense with fractions—that is, understanding the relative effect of different operations with fractions. Thus, please do not answer any of the questions by doing pencil-and-paper or calculator computations.

Part 1: Greater, smaller, equal, or depends?[6]

1.   In this question, x, y, and z are proper fractions (that is, their value is between 0 and 1). Fill in the blank with $<$, $>$, or "depends." If your answer is "depends," add a condition that will make $<$ or $>$ true. Briefly explain your reasoning.

   a. $x \cdot y \ \square \ x$ **b.** $x \cdot y \cdot z \ \square \ x$ **c.** $x \div y \ \square \ x$ **d.** $x \div y \ \square \ 1$

2.   In this question, x, y, and z are proper fractions and $0 < x < y < z$. Fill in the blank with $<$, $>$, or "depends." If your answer is "depends," add a condition that will make $<$ or $>$ true. Briefly explain your reasoning.

   a. $x \cdot y \ \square \ x$ **b.** $x \cdot y \cdot z \ \square \ x$ **c.** $x \div y \ \square \ x$ **d.** $x \div y \ \square \ y$

   e. $x \div y \ \square \ 1$

3.   After discussing your answers and justifications with your partner(s), note important things that you learned from wrong answers, from different answers, or from correct answers. Try to connect these reflections to fraction ideas.

---

[6] Adapted from Activity 25 in Reyes, et al., *Developing Number Sense in the Middle Grades.*

Part 2: Where is the answer on the number line?[7]

1. The points on the number line below are not drawn to scale. Without doing any computation, determine the region in which each answer will lie. Explain your reasoning.

  A   B   C   D   E

    0    $\frac{7}{13}$ $\frac{12}{17}$ 1

a. $\dfrac{7}{13} + \dfrac{12}{17}$ **b.** $\dfrac{7}{13} \cdot \dfrac{12}{17}$

c. $\dfrac{7}{13} \div \dfrac{12}{17}$ **d.** $\dfrac{12}{17} \div \dfrac{7}{13}$

2. After discussing your answers and justifications with your partner(s), note important things that you learned from wrong answers, from different answers, or from correct answers. Try to connect these reflections to fraction ideas.

Part 3: Where do the digits go?

1. Using four different digits, make two proper fractions whose sum will be as close as you can get to 1 but still less than 1.

$$\dfrac{\square}{\square} + \dfrac{\square}{\square}$$

2. Using four different digits, make two proper fractions whose difference will be as great as possible.

$$\dfrac{\square}{\square} - \dfrac{\square}{\square}$$

3. Using four different digits, make two proper fractions whose product will be as close as you can get to 1 but greater than 1.

$$\dfrac{\square}{\square} \times \dfrac{\square}{\square}$$

[7] This exploration has been adapted from one developed by the Summermath for Teachers program at Mt. Holyoke College and the Mathematics for Tomorrow project at Education Development Center.

4.   Using four different digits, make the smallest possible quotient.

$$\frac{\square}{\square} \div \frac{\square}{\square}$$

5.   After discussing your answers and justifications with your partner(s), note important things that you learned from wrong answers, from different answers, or from correct answers. Try to connect these reflections to fraction ideas.

EXPLORATION 5.10   **Wholes and Units: Not Always the Same**

Thinking of fractions only in terms of parts and wholes is simplistic and causes problems when we get beyond simple, routine problems. The following two problems will help you to grapple with some very important fraction ideas.

1.   **Absent Students.**[8] Let's say you are teaching. It is winter, and it seems that a larger fraction of students than normal are sick. You are eating lunch in the teachers' lounge and another teacher says, "In my class today, 2/5 of the girls were absent but only 1/5 of the boys were absent." What fraction of her class was absent today?

    a.   Write down your initial thoughts about this problem.

    b.   Meet with your partner(s) and discuss the problem. If you have the same answer, did you arrive at the answer in the same way? If you have different answers, listen to one another's reasoning until you can agree on one answer.

    c.   What is a realistic range of possible answers?

    d.   What is the theoretical range of possible answers?

2.   **How Much Is Her Share?**[9] This problem is adapted from a real-life problem. Josephine is a graduate student at Urban State College. Because her finances are limited, she has moved into a house with four other people. The house is heated with electricity, and the electric bill comes every two months. Josephine moved in on February 1. When the bill for January–February comes, what fraction of the bill should each person pay?

---

[8] This problem has been adapted from one developed by Deborah Schifter at Education Development Center.
[9] This problem has been adapted from a problem in *A Course Guide to Math 010L,* by Ron Narode, Deborah Schifter, and Jack Lochhead, 1985.

a. Work on this problem alone and show your work.

b. What assumptions did you make in order to solve this problem?

c. Meet with your partner(s) and discuss the problem. If you have the same answer, did you arrive at the answer in the same way? If you have different answers, listen to one another's reasoning until you can agree on one answer.

EXPLORATION 5.11   Meanings of Operations with Fractions[10]

The purpose of this exploration is to develop your operation sense by having you try to connect the problem with the operation.

Part 1: Matching problem situations with operations

Directions: For each of the seven problems below:

a. Represent the problem with a diagram.

b. Write a number sentence that would answer the question, *but do not determine the answer.*

c. Select the model that fits and briefly justify your choice:

+ combine, increase

− take-away, comparison, missing addend

× repeated addition, area, Cartesian product

÷ partitioning, repeated subtraction, missing factor

If none of the models fits, then explain how you knew which operation was appropriate.

Problems

1. A patient requires 3/4 of an ounce of medicine each day. If the bottle contains 12 ounces, how many days' supply does the patient have?

2. The label on a bottle of juice says that 3/4 of the bottle consists of apple juice, 1/6 of the bottle consists of cherry juice, and the rest is water. What fraction of the bottle is juice?

---

[10] This exploration is adapted from one developed by Ellen Davidson and Jim Hammerman at Education Development Center.

3.   Frieda had 12 inches of wire and cut pieces that were each 3/4 of an inch long. How many pieces does she have now?

4.   Jake had 12 cookies and ate 3/4 of them. How many cookies did he eat?

5.   Kareem had 12 gallons of ice cream in the freezer for his party. Last night Brad and Mary ate 3/4 of a gallon. How much ice cream is left?

6.   The Bassarear family is driving from home to a friend's house, and Emily and Josh are restless. They ask, "How far do we have to go?" Their father replies that they have gone 12 miles and that they are 3/4 of the way there. What is the distance from home to the friend's house?

7.   Karla has 3/4 of an acre of land for her garden. She has divided this garden into 12 equal regions. What is the size of each region?

Part 2: Connecting whole-number and fraction contexts

1.   For each of the models that were not used in the seven problems in Part 1, write a story problem or explain why that model is not possible for fractions.

2.   Some of the models (such as the combining context for addition) apply to fractions in the same way that they apply to whole numbers. However, some of the models do not work in the same way. Determine which models do not work in the same way and explain why. For example, let's say that you decided that the area model for multiplication of fractions works only if the fractions are proper fractions; explain why.

EXPLORATION 5.12   **Understanding and Creating Division Algorithms**[11]

Part 1: Invert and multiply

Most of you were taught the famous invert and multiply algorithm for dividing a fraction by a fraction. The purpose of this exploration is for you to understand why it works.

Directions

In each of the problems below, you need to:

a.   Represent the story with a diagram.

[11] This exploration has benefited from the influence of Ellen Davidson and Jim Hammesman at Education Development Center.

b. Explain how you can determine the quotient from the diagram. (*Note:* This requires explaining *why*, not just *what*.)

c. Write a number sentence involving division and connect each of its numbers to the problem.

d. Write a number sentence involving multiplication and connect each of its numbers to the problem.

Example

Jerome had 3 pounds of candy and decided to make 1/4-pound bags to give away. How many bags could he make with this candy?

a.

b. Each circle represents 1 pound of candy. I divided each pound into 4 regions (to make 1/4-pound bags). I solve the problem by counting the number of 1/4ths in the 3 pounds.

c. Number sentence with division: $3 \div 1/4$
The 3 represents the whole: 3 pounds.
The 1/4 represents the size of the part I am repeatedly taking away.

d. Number sentence with multiplication: $3 \cdot 4$
The 4 represents how many 1/4-pound bags per pound.
The 3 times 4 represents 4 bags per pound times 3 pounds.

Problems

1. A microscopic organism undertakes a journey of 2 inches. Each day the organism travels 1/5 inch. How many days will it take to finish the journey?

2. Pete's Painting Partnership has contracted to paint 4 houses. Each day the team can paint 2/3 of a house. How long will it take to finish all 4 houses?

3. Eno has 4 ounces of medicine. Each dose is 1 1/3 ounces. How many doses are there in the bottle?

Looking Back

How would you justify the invert and multiply algorithm now?

Part 2: Brahmagupta's algorithm

The famous Indian mathematician Brahmagupta described an algorithm for dividing fractions that is actually easier to understand, in terms of *why* it works, than the traditional invert and multiply algorithm. The purpose of this exploration is to help you to understand this algorithm and why it works.

For each of the problems below, first represent the problem with a diagram and then determine the answer from the diagram.

1.   Josie's Jammers have adopted a 4-mile stretch of highway to keep clean. Each afternoon they pick up trash. If they can clean 2/3 of a mile per day, how many days will it take to clean the whole section?

2.   Chien has 2/3 of a gallon of gasoline, and each time he mows the lawn, he uses 1/6 of a gallon. How many times can he mow the lawn before buying more gasoline?

3.   Jack has $7\frac{1}{2}$ pounds of dog food. Each day his dog eats $1\frac{1}{4}$ pounds. How many days' worth of dog food does he have?

4.   Rita has $3\frac{3}{4}$ ounces of perfume and wants to sell the perfume in 3/8-ounce bottles. How many bottles of perfume can she make?

Looking Back

Look at your solutions to each of the problems above.

1.   What do they all have in common?

2.   Looking at the commonalities, can you describe a rule that would allow you to solve any division problem? That is, what did you do to your whole so that you could repeatedly subtract the part? A hint is given at the end of Exploration 5.13.

E X P L O R A T I O N 5.13   **Remainders**

Recall the wire problem (Investigation 1.8). In many real-life situations, the remainder is as important as the quotient. The following exploration focuses on making sense of remainders with fractions.

Reconciling an Apparent Contradiction

1.   Marvin has 11 yards of cloth to make costumes for a play. Each costume requires $1\frac{1}{2}$ yards of material. How many costumes can he make?

a.   Represent and solve the problem with a diagram.

b. Solve the problem using the division algorithm.

2. Can you explain the fact that the diagram and the algorithm produce different answers?

Note: Most students find this to be a rather challenging question. Discuss the question with your partner(s) before reading on.

Different Ways to Express Remainders

3. Many students find going back and analyzing a simpler problem to be helpful. Consider the following problem: A doctor has 31 ounces of medicine, and each dose is 4 ounces. How many doses can the doctor make?

   a. When doing the computation, we can represent the answer as $7\frac{3}{4}$ or as 7 R3.

   b. What does the 3/4 mean?

   c. What does the R3 mean?

4. Now go back to Step 2. Write your present thinking about why we get two different answers.

5. When we divide two fractions in which the quotient is not a whole number, sometimes we are interested in the fraction that the algorithm produces (for example, 1/3 in the Marvin problem). In other cases, we are interested in the fraction that the diagram produces (for example, 1/2 in the Marvin problem). Make up two story problems, one in which the fraction that the algorithm produces is relevant, and one in which the fraction that the diagram produces is relevant.

   Hint for Brahmagupta's algorithm: Look at the denominator of the second fraction (divisor).

SECTION   5.4   **EXPLORING BEYOND INTEGERS AND FRACTIONS: DECIMALS, EXPONENTS, AND REAL NUMBERS**

There is much evidence that many students' understanding of decimals is mostly procedural. That is, they can compute with decimals, but their understanding of decimals is only weakly connected to their understanding of whole numbers and fractions and weakly connected to what the four fundamental operations mean. The following explorations will help you build stronger connections among many of the key concepts underlying operations with decimals.

EXPLORATION 5.14   **Decimals and Base 10 Blocks**

Connecting Decimals to Base 10 Blocks

For the following questions, you will need base 10 blocks.

1.   If the flat has a value of 1, represent 0.24 in two different ways. Justify your answers.

2.   Represent 4.32 in two different ways. Specify your choice of unit for each representation.

3.   Represent 0.0127 in two different ways. Justify your answers. Specify your choice of unit for each representation.

4.   Demonstrate 0.463 + 0.507 with base 10 blocks. Justify each step.

5.   Demonstrate 0.802 − 0.568 with base 10 blocks. Justify each step.

6.   Show why 0.1 × 0.1 = 0.01 with base 10 blocks.

7.   Demonstrate the equality of 0.1, 0.10, and 0.100 with base 10 blocks.

Greater Than or Less Than?

8.   Insert < or > between each pair of numbers, and justify your choice:
   a. 0.5   0.28

   b. 8.3   8.14

c. 2.43   2.4168

d. 0.07   0.068

e. 6.74   6.74003

EXPLORATION 5.15   **Patterns in Repeating Decimals**

When we convert some fractions to decimals, we find that some "terminate" and some "repeat." For example, convert 1/11 and 1/16 to decimals with your calculator.

$$1/16 = 0.0625 \quad \text{but} \quad 1/11 = 0.0909090909090909 \ldots$$

Rather than writing the "dot dot dot," we place a bar over the portion that repeats, and we represent 1/11 as $0.\overline{09}$.

How would you represent 2/3 and 7/15?

Part 1: Predicting the next number in a sequence

1.   We used a calculator above to determine the value of 1/11.

   a.   Predict the value of 2/11 and explain your reasoning.

   Now use the calculator to determine the value of 2/11.

   If your prediction was correct, great. If not, look back at your reasoning and see if you can modify it (like finding a bug in a computer program). Describe your insights.

   b.   Predict the value of 3/11 and explain your reasoning. Then determine the value of 3/11. If your prediction was correct, great. If not, analyze your thinking.

   c.   Describe the pattern you see in words. If you do not see a pattern, determine the value of 4/11, 5/11, and so on until you do see a pattern.

   d.   Predict the value of 9/11 and explain your reasoning. Then determine the value of 9/11. If your prediction was correct, great. If not, analyze your thinking.

e. Predict the value of 10/11 and explain your reasoning. Then determine the value of 10/11. If your prediction was correct, great. If not, analyze your thinking.

2. Use a calculator to determine the value of 1/15.

   a. Predict the value of 2/15 and explain your reasoning. Then determine the value of 2/15. If your prediction was correct, great. If not, analyze your thinking.

   b. Predict the value of 3/15 and explain your reasoning. Then determine the value of 3/15. If your prediction was correct, great. If not, analyze your thinking.

   c. Predict the value of 4/15 and explain your reasoning. Then determine the value of 4/15. If your prediction was correct, great. If not, analyze your thinking.

   d. Describe the pattern you see in words. If you do not see a pattern, determine the value of 5/15, 6/15, and so on until you do see a pattern.

   e. Predict the value of 14/15 and explain your reasoning. Then determine the value of 14/15. If your prediction was correct, great. If not, analyze your thinking.

3. Use a calculator to determine the value of 1/99.

   a. Predict the value of 2/99 and explain your reasoning. Then determine the value of 2/99. If your prediction was correct, great. If not, analyze your thinking.

   b. Predict the value of 3/99 and explain your reasoning. Then determine the value of 3/99. If your prediction was correct, great. If not, analyze your thinking.

   c. Describe the pattern you see in words. If you do not see a pattern, determine the value of 4/99, 5/99, and so on until you do see a pattern.

d. Predict the value of 9/99 and explain your reasoning. Then determine the value of 9/99. If your prediction was correct, great. If not, analyze your thinking.

e. Predict the value of 10/99 and explain your reasoning. Then determine the value of 10/99. If your prediction was correct, great. If not, analyze your thinking.

f. Predict the value of 43/99 and explain your reasoning. Then determine the value of 43/99. If your prediction was correct, great. If not, analyze your thinking.

4. Now we will look at the set of fractions whose denominator is 999.

a. Based on your work in Step 3, can you predict the value of 1/999? If so, explain the reasoning behind your hypothesis. Then determine the value of 1/999 using pencil and paper.

b. Predict the value of 2/999 and explain your reasoning. Then determine the value of 2/999. If your prediction was correct, great. If not, analyze your thinking.

c. Continue this process until you see a pattern. Then describe the pattern you see in words.

5. Now we will look at the set of fractions whose denominator is 101.

a. Based on your work, can you predict the value of 1/101? If so, explain the reasoning behind your hypothesis. Then determine the value of 1/101 using pencil and paper.

b. Predict the value of 2/101 and explain your reasoning. Then determine the value of 2/101. If your prediction was correct, great. If not, analyze your thinking.

c. Continue this process until you see a pattern. Then describe the pattern you see in words.

Part 2: When will a decimal terminate and when will it repeat?

Now that you have some experience with converting fractions to decimals, we will investigate a question that fascinated mathematicians several hundred years ago: Can we predict whether the decimal equivalent of a fraction will terminate or repeat?

1. Write down your present thoughts as hypotheses. For example, if the denominator is an even number, its decimal equivalent will terminate, and so on.

2. **a.** With your partners, determine a plan to test your hypotheses.

   b. Meet with another group and share your ideas.

   c. Describe your plan.

3. Collect your data. That is, select a fraction and predict whether it will terminate or repeat. Then do the computation. At the right, note any insights from your work. Your sheet should look something like this:

Number	Prediction	Analysis/insight
5/13	Repeat because odd number	It repeats.

4. Write down your current hypotheses, and justify them.

EXPLORATION 5.16   **Precision and Decimals**

As mentioned in the textbook, one of the reasons for the development of fractions and decimals was that whole numbers are simply not precise enough for many situations. The purpose of this exploration is to better understand the magnitude of the invention of decimals and the invention of the metric system.

For this exploration, you will need a ruler with inches on one side and centimeters on the other side.

1. Select a rectangular region to measure—for example, the front cover of this textbook, the front cover of a notebook, a sheet of paper (not 8 1/2 by 11 inches).

   a. Measure the dimensions of the region to the nearest inch.

   b. Determine the area.

2. **a.** Measure the dimensions of the region you chose for this exploration as accurately as you can, using the inches side of the ruler.

    b. Represent the area in the form $a\frac{b}{c}$ square inches.

3. **a.** Measure the dimensions of the region as accurately as you can, using the centimeter side of the ruler.

    b. Represent the area as a decimal.

4. Determine a means to convert square centimeters to square inches or use the conversion your instructor gives you.

5. Compare the three values. Which value do you think is closest to the actual area? Why?

6. Describe a real-life situation in which the accuracy given by inches and fractions of inches is not sufficient.

EXPLORATION 5.17   **Place Value: A Decimal Game**

While most students can manipulate decimals (that is, add, subtract, multiply, and divide) with reasonable accuracy, there is much evidence that few students have a sophisticated number sense (such as being able to estimate) with respect to decimals. The NCTM recognizes that number sense is an essential tool for students to develop. The primary goal of each of the four games in Explorations 5.17 through 5.20 is for you to develop and refine your decimal number sense. It is important that you remember that the goal is not to score the most points, but rather to constantly monitor your own decimal sense, asking questions like:

      What tools do I have to help me estimate decimal computations?
      How is my ability to estimate related to my understanding of decimals?

The Game
This game requires you to pay attention to place value and to think about the relationship between the places. It can be played cooperatively or competitively.

Directions for playing the game:
- Note the target number (for this game).
- Make a table like the one below. (*Note:* The places will vary depending on the places in the target number.)

Sum of the dice	10th	100th	1000th	Cumulative sum

- Roll two standard dice and write the sum of their values in one of the three place value columns. Exceptions: if the sum is 10, write a 0. If the sum is 11 or 12, write a 1.
- Record your cumulative sum in the last column.
- Repeat the last two steps until the game stops (explained below).
- The goal is to get as close as possible to the target number without going over the target number.
- The game stops when you go over the target number.
  Example of a record for one game (target number = 0.85):

Sum of the dice	10th	100th	Cumulative sum
6		6	0.06
8	8		0.86

1. Game 1: The target number is 8.00. The chart will have columns for ones, tenths, and hundredths.

2. Game 2: The target number is 78.42. The chart will have columns for tens, ones, tenths, and hundredths.

3. Make up your own target numbers and play more games.

Looking Back on Exploration 5.17

1. What if the new target number was 8.117? Describe and justify your overall "game plan."

2. Describe your most important learning from this game.

EXPLORATION 5.18 **The Right Bucket: A Decimal Game**

This game comes from *Ideas from the Arithmetic Teacher: Grades 6–8,*[12] one of many useful books published by the National Council of Teachers of Mathematics. It can be played alone or with a partner, competitively or cooperatively.

---

[12] George Immerzeel and Melvin Thomas eds., *Ideas from the Arithmetic Teacher: Grades 6–8* (Reston, Va.: NCTM, 1982), p. 45.

Directions for playing the game:

- Select two decimals from the list below and cross them off the list.
- Multiply the two decimals.
- Determine your score by looking at the bucket chart below. For example, products between 10 and 100 earn a score of 2 points.
- Select two more decimals, find their product, and determine your score. Continue until you have used all the decimals.
- The goal is to score as many points as you can.

Bucket Chart

The learning value of this game comes from refining your ability to estimate. (You may want to reread the introduction to Exploration 5.17.)

3.6	0.03	13.1	29.6	11.9	0.7	33.7
0.04	21.9	.125	10.1	0.42	0.07	2.9
0.29	19.5	5.52	23.1	9.6	1.8	

1. First Game

   a. Play the game in the following manner. In a table like the one below, select two decimals, show your estimate, and explain the reasoning for your selection.

Turn	Decimals	Estimate	Reasoning	Points
1				
2				
3				
4				
5				
6				

Turn	Decimals	Estimate	Reasoning	Points
7				
8				
9				
10				
			Total	

b. If you are playing competitively, record each person's actual scores for every round played and find each person's total score. The greatest total score wins. If you are playing cooperatively, record the team's ten actual scores and total score.

c. What did you learn about estimating and mental math with decimals from this game?

2. Second game. Play the game over (a few times, if you wish), this time cooperatively. Your goal is to get the maximum number of total points.

a. Is it possible to choose the pairs of decimals so that you can get 3 points each time? If you think so, explain why. If you think not, explain why not.

b. Describe your maximum game in a table like the one below.

Turn	Decimals	Estimate	Reasoning	Points
1				
2				
3				
4				

Turn	Decimals	Estimate	Reasoning	Points
5				
6				
7				
8				
9				
10				
			Total	

c. Describe the different strategies that you used to determine which pairs of decimals to put together.

d. What did you learn during the process of trying to find the maximum score?

3. Third game. Play another game with the following decimals.

0.023	0.9	5.74	0.245	7.3	1.2
23.8	16.5	0.068	8.7	0.12	
1.8	0.78	42.7	0.2	3.6	

a. Record your scores in a table like the one below.

Turn	Decimals	Estimate	Reasoning	Points
1				
2				
3				

Turn	Decimals	Estimate	Reasoning	Points
4				
5				
6				
7				
8				
9				
10				
			Total	

b. Describe any new strategies you devised from playing this game.

4.   Fourth game.
   a. Make up a new set of decimals and determine the maximum score that can be obtained, using your decimals.

   b. Give your decimals to another team and have them determine the maximum score they can create.

Looking Back on Exploration 5.18

1.   What did you learn about number sense with decimals?

2.   Why is decimal number sense important?

EXPLORATION 5.19 **Operations: A Decimal Game**

This game requires you to examine the effects of the four operations on decimal computation. As you move through the games, you should see improvement. At the end of each game, you will be asked to stop and reflect on your improvement.

Directions for playing the game

1. Make up four decimal numbers — for example, 3.6, 45.3, 1.23, 0.005.

2. From your list, select the three decimals that will make the answer to the equation below as large as possible. Describe your strategy in words.

$$\square + \square - \square =$$

For example, 45.3 + 3.6 − 0.005. Description of strategy: "I picked the two largest decimals to add and then picked the smallest decimal to subtract because I wanted to take away as little as possible."

3. If you are confident that you have the maximum number, go to Step 4. If not, try other combinations of numbers until you feel you have the combination that produces the largest number.

4. Make up four new decimal numbers. Give your strategy to another group. Have them use your strategy.
   Now check: Does this strategy produce the largest number?
   If yes, move on. If not, revise your strategy, and repeat Step 2.

1. First game.

   a. Make up four decimal numbers.

   b. Select the three decimals that will make the answer to the equation below as large as possible.

   $$\square \times \square + \square =$$

   Describe your strategy in words.

   c. If you are confident that you have the maximum number, go to Step 1(d). If not, try other combinations of numbers until you feel you have the combination that produces the largest number.

   d. Make up four new decimal numbers. Give your strategy to another group. Have them use your strategy to select the three decimals.

   Now check: Does this produce the largest number?

If yes, move on. If not, revise your strategy, and repeat Step 1(b).

2. Second game.

    a. Make up four decimal numbers.

    b. Select the three decimals that will make the answer to the equation below as *small* as possible.

    $$\boxed{} \times \boxed{} \div \boxed{} =$$

    Describe your strategy in words.

    c. If you are confident that you have the minimum number, go to Step 2(d). If not, try other combinations of numbers until you feel you have the combination that produces the smallest number.

    d. Make up four new decimal numbers. Give your strategy to another group. Have them use your strategy to select the three decimals.

    Now check: Does this produce the smallest number?

    If yes, move on. If not, revise your strategy, and repeat Step 2(b).

    e. Would your strategy change if we added parentheses?

    $$\boxed{} \times \left(\boxed{} \div \boxed{}\right) =$$

    Describe your hypothesis before doing any computations with the calculator. Then do some computations and decide whether to keep your original hypothesis or to revise it.

3. Third game.

    a. Write an equation, but this time you pick the operations.

    b. Make up four decimal numbers.

c. Select the three decimals that will make the answer to your equation as large (or as small) as possible.

d. Make up four new decimal numbers. Give your strategy to another group. Have them use your strategy to select the three decimals.

Now check: Does this produce the highest answer?

If yes, move on. If not, revise your strategy, and repeat Step 3(c).

Looking Back on Exploration 5.19

1. Describe the most important thing you learned about decimals and operations during this game.

2. Does your strategy depend on the numbers chosen? For example, for the sample exploration, we would pick the two largest numbers to put in the first two boxes and the smallest number for the third box, regardless of the numbers. Is there a simple, general strategy for every game?

EXPLORATION 5.20   **Target: A Decimal Game**

Directions for playing the game:
Select a number, an operation, a goal, and a winning zone; for example:

Starting number	145
Operation	multiplication
Goal	1
Winning zone	0.9 to 1.1 (or 0.99 to 1.01, or 1 to 1.1)

The winner is the one who gets the answer (in this case, the product) in the zone.
Player 1 begins with the starting number and selects a number to multiply the starting number by that will result in the product of the two numbers being in the winning zone (in this case between 0.9 and 1.1). The player then multiplies the starting number (145) by the second number. This product is now the second player's starting number. Play continues until the product is within the winning zone.

Computation	Product	Reasoning
145×0.006	0.87	I knew that 100×0.01 would be 1. Since 145 is bigger than 100, I picked a number smaller than 0.01.

1.   Play several games with a partner. Record your results, using the format shown below.

Starting number   ___
Operation   _____
Goal   _____
Winning zone   ___ to ___

Turn	Computation	Product	Reasoning
1			
2			
3			
4			
5			

2.   Describe one mental math strategy that you learned during this game.

Proportional Reasoning

The following explorations require you to grapple with ratios, rates, proportions, and percents, all of which fall under the big idea of proportional reasoning. It is ironic that while we probably find the need to use proportional reasoning in our everyday lives as much as we do any other kind of mathematical reasoning, a substantive body of research shows that few adults can competently and confidently navigate nonroutine problems involving proportional reasoning.

SECTION 6.1 **EXPLORING RATIO AND PROPORTION**

In this section, you will explore real-life applications of ratio and proportions, examine the connection between proportions and functions, and grapple with the very meaning of ratios and proportions.

EXPLORATION 6.1 **Unit Pricing**

Unit pricing is now common. Underneath most items in grocery stores is the unit price of the item. For example, if a 24-ounce jar of pickles costs $2.79, the unit price is 11.6¢, which means that the pickles cost 11.6¢ per ounce, which is equivalent to $.116 per ounce.

If you don't see that 11.6¢ = $.116, STOP. Assess your understanding. Are you on solid ground, are you on shaky ground, or are you lost? If you are on shaky ground or lost, what can you do to connect to the material? What do you know that could help you understand? For instance, you might see that

10¢ = $.10

So   11¢ = $.11

Thus   11.6¢ = $.116

Many states now require grocery stores to show the unit price below each item. One of the reasons for this law is that people tend to believe that larger items are proportionally cheaper. For example, they believe that a 64-ounce box of detergent will cost less than twice as much as a 32-ounce box. However, many companies used this belief to their advantage.

1. Let's say you have Paul Bunyan pancake mix in two sizes: 30 ounces and 50 ounces. The smaller box costs $2.89, and the larger box costs $4.69.

   a. Without using a calculator, determine which is the better buy. Record your process.

   b. Use a calculator and record your process.

   c. Jackie did the problem this way:

   $$\frac{30}{2.89} = 10.38 \qquad \frac{50}{4.69} = 10.66$$

   What labels belong with 10.38 and 10.66? In other words, what do those numbers mean?

   What do you think of Jackie's method? Justify your response.

   d. Describe three situations in which you might buy the smaller item even if it cost more proportionally than the larger item.

EXPLORATION 6.2   **Buying Generic**

An issue related to unit pricing is generic products. In recent years, the sale of generic brands has increased tremendously. When I was growing up in the 1950s and 1960s, consumers could choose among the various name brands. Now, however, consumers can choose among the name brands or choose the generic alternative. Talk among your group. Are there products for which you are more likely to buy the generic brand? What about products for which you are not likely to buy the generic brand? What reasons do you give for choosing to buy the generic brand or choosing to buy the name brand?

1. One of the obvious reasons for buying the generic brand is that it is cheaper. In this exploration, we will examine how we can determine how much cheaper. Let's say you go to a store and you see a dispenser of Scotch brand tape that sells for $1.69 and a generic alternative that sells for $1.29. Both rolls contain the same amount of tape.

a. How could we compare the two prices? Discuss this in your group and write down your thoughts.

b. Describe and critique different ways in which we could compare the two prices.

2. Let's extend this question.

a. Select a drugstore and collect and compare data on a name-brand pain reliever and a generic brand (or compare newspaper ads). Suppose you were writing an advertisement for the drugstore and you wanted to convince shoppers that they could save a lot of money by buying the generic pain reliever. Would your comparisons use addition or subtraction? (We will later call these comparisons *additive.*) Would they use multiplication, percents, or ratios? (We will later call these comparisons *multiplicative.*) Write the ad.

b. Gather data on different sizes. Do you always get more for your money with the bigger size?

c. Gather data from two different stores. How much cheaper is one store than the other?

3. Let's say an average family of 4 decided to buy generic whenever possible. Over the course of a year, how much money would they save?

E X P L O R A T I O N   6.3   **Proportional Reasoning and Functions**

In this exploration, we will explore a variety of functions that rely on proportional reasoning.

1. Solve each of the problems below.

a. It costs Rita 50¢ for the first three minutes of a long-distance call to her boyfriend and 20¢ for each additional minute. If Rita calls her boyfriend and talks for 12 minutes, how much does the call cost?

b. At Sam's Submarine Sandwich Shop, the cost of your submarine sandwich is determined by the length of the sandwich. If Sam charges $2 per foot, how much will a 20-inch sandwich cost?

c. The first grade class is measuring the length of a dinosaur by using students' footsteps. The first dinosaur is 6 of Alisha's footsteps and 9 of Carlo's footsteps. If the second dinosaur is 8 of Alisha's footsteps, how many of Carlo's footsteps will it be?

d. A farmer has determined that he has enough hay for 4 cows for 3 weeks. If the farmer suddenly obtains 2 more cows, how long can he expect the hay to last?

e. A kind of bacteria can double in 1 hour. If we start with 1 bacterium, how many bacteria will there be after 20 hours?

f. Consider the set of quadrinumbers below. How many dots does the 5th quadrinumber contain?

2. Discuss solutions and strategies for each of the six problems in Step 1 with your partner(s).

3. Determine a general formula for each problem below. Then discuss solutions and strategies for each problem.

a. If it costs 50 cents for the first 3 minutes and x cents for each additional minute, and a person talks for y minutes, what is the cost?

b. If the sandwich costs x dollars per foot and it is y inches long, what is the cost?

c. If the first dinosaur is 6 of Alisha's footsteps and 8 of Carlo's footsteps, and another dinosaur is x of Alisha's footsteps, how many of Carlo's footsteps will it be?

d. If there is enough hay for 4 cows for 3 weeks, how long would the hay last if there were x cows?

e. If bacteria double every hour, how many bacteria will there be after x hours? Start with 1 bacterium.

f. How many dots are in the *x*th quadrinumber?

4. For each problem, construct a graph that shows the relationship between the variables. Describe each graph as if you were talking to someone on the phone.

5. Describe the similarities and differences among these six problems that you see. For example, the graphs of some families are straight lines and the graphs of others are not.

E X P L O R A T I O N 6.4 **Safety First?**

Take a few minutes to examine the data below. Then respond to the questions that follow.

DEATHS FROM ACCIDENTS IN THE UNITED STATES

Year	Motor vehicles	Falls	Fires and burns	Drowning	Firearms	Drugs and medicine	Ingestion or inhalation of objects
1970	54,633	16,926	6,718	6,391	2,406	2,505	2,753
1990	46,814	12,313	4,175	3,979	1,416	4,506	3,303

1. What observations do you make from this set of data? If someone were to ask you what you see from these data, what would you say?

2. Describe at least two questions you might ask of the person who collected these data. One question needs to deal with the validity of the data.

3. The figures below show the same data, but in a slightly different form.

DEATH RATES FROM ACCIDENTS IN THE UNITED STATES
RATE PER 100,000 POPULATION

Year	Motor vehicles	Falls	Fires and burns	Drowning	Firearms	Drugs and medicine	Ingestion or inhalation of objects
1970	26.9	8.3	3.3	3.1	1.2	1.2	1.4
1990	18.8	5.0	1.7	1.6	0.6	1.8	1.3

How do you think the numbers in the second set of data were determined?

4. Explain, as if you were talking to someone who doesn't understand, what the second set of numbers mean. For example, what does a motor vehicle death rate of 26.9 mean?

5.   Let's say you were writing a newspaper article on changes in accidental deaths over this period and the editor said that because of space limitations, you could show either the raw numbers or the rates, but not both. Summarize the pros and cons of each representation.

6.   Cecilia has a question. The number of deaths from ingestion or inhalation of objects rose from 2,753 to 3,303, and that is a 20% increase. So how can the rate have gone down?

7.   Using only the data from the two tables, can you determine the U.S. population in 1970?

8.   Select one column and predict whether you would expect the death rate to be higher or lower now than in 1990. Briefly explain your reasoning.

9.   If you look at newspapers and magazines, you sometimes see raw data and sometimes see rates. For example, an article might discuss the number of births or the number of crimes, or it might discuss the birth rate or the crime rate. Explain, as if you were talking to someone who has not taken this course, the need for rates. What do rates mean? Why do we have them, and what purpose do they serve?

E X P L O R A T I O N 6.5   **Which Ramp Is Steeper?**

As we have discussed in the book, one of the uses of mathematics is to compare. In some cases, the comparison is easy — who is taller. In the following case, the comparison is not quite so simple. An exploration commonly done with elementary school students has them roll carts down ramps to examine the relationship between the steepness of the ramp and the distance the cart travels. In this exploration, we will focus on one aspect of this experiment — comparing the steepness of different ramps.
     Suppose the students weren't told to standardize measurements, and each pair's ramp had different dimensions. For example, one pair had a ramp with height of 14 cm, a base of 23 cm, and a ramp of 26.9 cm. Another pair had a ramp with height of 12 cm, a base of 18 cm, and a ramp of 21.6 cm. One student hypothesized that the steeper the ramp, the further the marbles would go, and this prompted a desire to rank the slopes according to steepness. The students didn't want to build the ramps all over again, but each pair had the following measurements: length of base (B), height of base (H), and length of ramp (R).

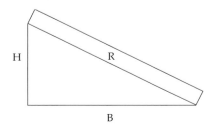

1. Develop a method for determining the relative steepness of the various ramps. *Note:* You are not given the students' actual data. Your job is to develop a plan. This task requires scientific thinking, and the following process is suggested:

   a. First, brainstorm different hypotheses to determine relative steepness.

   b. Second, discuss the pros and cons of those hypotheses that one or more members of the group feel are worth pursuing.

   c. Last, select one hypothesis and discuss a method for determining its validity. For example, let's say you pursue method x for determining which of 2 slopes is steeper. What do you need to do in order to determine whether this method is valid or not valid? Obviously, one way to assess a method is to determine sample data and then construct actual ramps from those data. What else might you do, short of constructing actual models to assess your hypothesis? If you make up sample data, note that the value of R can be determined by $R = \sqrt{H^2 + B^2}$.

2. Meet with another group to compare hypotheses. If your hypotheses are identical, discuss your method for assessing the hypothesis. If your hypotheses are different, debate the two hypotheses until you come to a conclusion — one group decides that its hypothesis is not valid, each group decides that its hypothesis is or is not valid, or you reach an impasse.

3. Consider the data from two ramps:

Ramp	Height	Base	Ramp
A	8 cm	20 cm	21.5 cm
B	12 cm	26 cm	28.6 cm

   Use your present method to predict which ramp is steeper. If another group has a different hypothesis, debate with that group to determine if both hypotheses are valid, both are invalid, or one is valid and the other invalid.

4. After the discussion with other groups, do you wish to revise your hypothesis? If so, what convinced you that your previous hypothesis was not valid?

5. Your instructor will select one or more hypotheses for you to critique (that is, to examine carefully). For each hypothesis, decide whether you believe it is or is not valid. If you think it is valid, explain why. If you think it is not valid, explain why not or give a counterexample. If you think the hypothesis is invalid but has merit,

try to modify it so that it is valid. Explain why you think the modified hypothesis is now valid.

6. Now the class has a new problem. Let's say most of the groups doing the experiment recorded their data in inches, but some groups used centimeters. Can we determine the relative steepness with their data, or do we first have to convert one set of data into the other unit—for example, centimeters to inches? Why or why not?

SECTION   6.2   **EXPLORING PERCENTS**

Open the newspaper on any given day and you will probably find percents used in more than one story on the front page. Percents are a powerful tool that enable us to compare amounts and to describe change.

EXPLORATION 6.6   **Percents**

Sales

John sees that the local department store is having a sale. He goes to the store and finds that all televisions are 25% off.
1. Describe in words what that means.

2. Let's say he is interested in a particular television that normally sells for $400. If it is 25% off, how much will he pay for it?

3. There are two common ways in which students solve this problem.
    - Ann: 25% of $400 is $100. $400 − $100 = $300. John pays $300.
    - Bela: 75% of $400 is $300. John pays $300.

    Ann doesn't understand what Bela did. How can you help her? You may, if you wish, use the diagram at the right.

4. Let's say that Joe gets a 5% raise and that he presently makes $8.00 per hour. One way to determine his new wage is to find 5% of 8.00 and then add that to 8.00. Using the ideas generated above, can you figure out how to determine his new wage with only one calculation? Describe the method.

Percent Decrease and Increase

Joshua is confused. He works for the Adamson Printing Company. Last year the economy was in such bad shape that all employees agreed to take a 20% cut in pay.

However, this year the economy had improved so much that the company agreed to give everyone a 20% raise. Before the pay cut, Joshua was making $30,000 a year.

5. Explain why the 20% raise does not "undo" the 20% pay cut.

6. What raise would undo the 20% pay cut?

7. Determine a general formula that will tell you what percent increase will undo an x percent decrease.

Changes in Rates

In New Hampshire, where I live, there was a tremendous amount of controversy over the Seabrook nuclear power plant. The construction of the plant was held up many times. Eventually the company that made the reactor went bankrupt. It was bought out by another utility company. Part of the deal to ensure that the new company would make a profit was that it could increase rates by *at least* 5.5% each year for 7 years.

8. Bill and Betty Olsen figured that their average monthly electric bill last year was $83.21.

   a. If they use, on average, the same amount of electricity over the next 7 years, and their bill increases exactly 5.5% each year, what can they expect their utility bill to be at the end of 7 years?

   b. Meet with your partner(s) and discuss answers and solutions. If you think you would change your method in order to do a similar problem, describe how and why the new method works.

   c. Jarrad used the following method:

   $83.21 \times 0.055 = 4.57655$
   $83.21 + 4.58 = 87.79$
   $87.79 \times 0.055 = \text{etc.}$

   Do you think Jarrad's method is valid? Why or why not?

   What suggestions would you give to Jarrad? Justify your suggestions.

9. Last year the Olsens' combined income was $42,310. If their income increases by 5.5% each year, what would their income be at the end of 7 years?

EXPLORATION 6.7   **Single-Parent Family**

One of the major learnings my students report from working with real-life data is that people can distort the reader's impression of data both by the way in which the data are given and by not giving certain numbers. Let us work through an interesting example.

1.   Consider the following data: In 1980, women were the head of 6,230,000 single-parent families. By 1992, women were the head of 9,028,000 single-parent families. Describe your first interpretations of the data.

2.   Now consider the following data: In 1980, men were the head of 690,000 single-parent families. By 1992, men were the head of 1,472,000 single-parent families.

   a.   How does this information change your perception of how single-parent families are changing?

   b.   Write a short article, as if for a daily newspaper, interpreting the changing nature of the single-parent family over this period of time. You need to decide how you want to interpret the change (additively, multiplicatively, or some other way), show and justify any computations you do, and then write the news article.

   c.   Exchange papers with someone in your group and critique your partner's work with respect to accuracy and clarity.

EXPLORATION 6.8   **Mice on Two Islands**

There are two different islands in the Southern Micific Ocean, Azumi and Muremi, each of which has 20,000 mice. In this exploration, we will explore different ways in which populations can change.

1.   Brainstorm factors that could affect the rate of growth of the mouse populations.

2.   Let's say that the factors on Azumi produce an environment in which the population grows by 3,000 each year, and the factors on Muremi produce an environment in which the population grows by 10% each year. That is, in Azumi's case, we can determine the next year's population additively; in Muremi's case, we can determine the next year's population multiplicatively.
       A quick computation shows that after one year, Azumi will have more mice— 23,000, compared to Muremi's mouse population of 22,000. Do you think that Azumi will always have more mice than Muremi (disregarding factors like disease and predators)? Why or why not?

3.   a. Determine a method for finding the annual mouse populations of the two islands for the next 15 years.

b. Determine the annual populations and compare answers and solutions with your partner(s).

c. If you found errors in your method, note them and explain the cause of the error. If you find that you prefer someone else's method, explain and justify the new method.

4. Let us focus now not on the numbers of mice on each island, but on the relationship between the two populations. We can then use this information to extrapolate into the future.

a. Let us examine two different ways to compare the relative sizes of the populations of the two islands. We could make a table showing the difference between the two populations, or we could make a table showing the ratio of the two populations. Make the two tables, and then graph the results on two different graphs. Explain each graph as if you were talking to someone who missed this exploration.

b. Each graph is useful for answering different kinds of questions. For example, which graph would you use to answer the following question: How much larger will Muremi's mouse population be in five years? Which graph would help you predict when Muremi's mouse population will be 50% greater than Azumi's mouse population? Explain your answers.

c. Compare your predictions with those of your partner(s). As always, if you want to change something as a result of the discussion, identify the change you wish to make and justify it.

EXPLORATION 6.9[1]   **Do You Get What You Pay For?**

There are a number of items that you buy by the pound, although you are paying for parts of the items that you don't use. For example, you throw out the shells from peanuts, the husks and cobs from corn, the rind of the watermelon, the bones from chicken, and the peels from oranges. Just what percent of the product are you tossing out?

1. Let us begin with oranges. In this step, we will only plan a procedure. Data collection takes place in Step 2.

---

[1] This exploration is adapted from one developed by Nancy Belsky.

a. Design a procedure to find out what percent of the weight of an orange is peel.

b. What assumptions did you make in designing your procedure? (For example, not all oranges will have the same percentage of peel; like humans, some have thicker skins!)

c. Exchange descriptions of the procedure with another person (group). Make comments on the validity of that person or group's procedure and the clarity of the description. Listen to the comments about your procedure.

d. What changes would you make in your procedure now that you have compared it with one or more other procedures?

2. Using the procedure designed in Step 1, carry out the experiment to find the percentage of an orange that you throw away.

a. Describe your data. Show your results.

b. Compare your results with those of other groups or of the whole class.

c. Is there anything that you would change about the design of your experiment? If so, explain your changes.

d. What did you learn from this exploration?

Extensions

3. Do you think the grower makes more or less profit from thick-skinned oranges than from thin-skinned ones? Explain your reasoning.

4. Do you think grapefruits, in general, would have a higher percentage of peel than oranges? What about lemons? Explain your answer.

5. Describe how you would find the percent of waste for peeled apples.

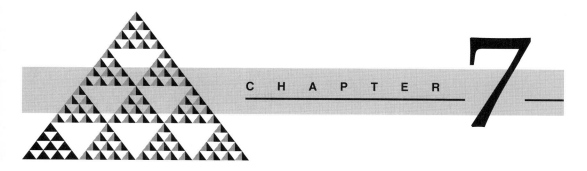

Uncertainty: Data and Chance

The explorations in this chapter have been designed to provide you with meaningful experiences involving the collection and interpretation of data and the performance of probability experiments so that you can grapple with some of the basic ideas in the fields of statistics and probability. I want you to experience the excitement that I have seen elementary and college students feel when they suddenly see something when graphing a set of data that they didn't see simply from looking at the numbers, or when they see patterns in chance phenomena that enable them to have a better sense of the probability of that event happening.

SECTION 7.1 **EXPLORING, REPRESENTING, AND INTERPRETING DATA**

Statistical ideas can help you to understand data that someone else has gathered. Many people tend to accept the data they read as true. However, it is quite common for data to be inaccurate or invalid. It is important that when you look at a set of data, you think about what the data mean, who collected the data, how the data were collected, and the like. We speak of the reliability of the data; that is, if two different groups were to collect the data, would they get the "same" numbers? We also speak of the validity of the data; that is, are the methods used to collect the data valid? In each of the following explorations, you will be presented with a set of data, and you will make and interpret graphs from those data. In each case, you will first be asked for your initial impressions of the data and questions you have about the data; sometimes the impressions will be insights, and sometimes they will be surprises. Don't be afraid to ask about reliability, validity, and numbers or sentences that you don't understand.

EXPLORATION 7.1   **Population Growth, Population Density, and Area of Residence**

Did you know that the framers of the U.S. Constitution required, in Article 1, Section 2, that a census be taken every ten years? Their concept of representative government relies on knowing just who is being represented! The data these censuses collect are a window into our world.

Population Growth

1. Look at the data at the right and write down your initial impressions; that is, write at least one sentence and not more than a paragraph describing what you "see" from these numbers. Then compare your impressions with your partner(s).

2. Let us focus first on the total population numbers.

    a. If you were to describe the growth of the U.S. population over the last 50 years, what would you say? That is, can you be more precise than simply saying, "The population is increasing"? For example, if you say, "It is increasing fast," what do you mean by "fast"?

    b. Predict the population in the year 2000 based on these numbers. Briefly explain how you came up with your number.

U.S. POPULATION, POPULATION DENSITY, AND AREA OF RESIDENCE, 1790–1990

Year	Total population	Percent increase	Pop. per sq. mi.	Percent urban	Percent rural
1790	3,929,214	N.A.	4.5	5.1%	94.9%
1800	5,308,483	35.1%	6.1	6.1	93.9
1810	7,239,881	36.4	4.3	7.3	92.7
1820	9,638,453	33.1	5.5	7.2	92.8
1830	12,866,020	33.5	7.4	8.8	91.2
1840	17,069,453	32.7	9.8	10.8	89.2
1850	23,191,876	35.9	7.9	15.3	84.7
1860	31,443,321	35.6	10.6	19.8	80.2
1870	39,818,449	26.6	13.4	25.7	74.3
1880	50,155,783	26.0	16.9	28.2	71.8
1890	62,947,714	25.5	21.2	35.1	64.9
1900	75,994,575	20.7	25.6	39.6	60.4
1910	91,972,266	21.0	31.0	45.6	54.4
1920	105,710,620	14.9	35.6	51.2	48.8
1930	122,775,046	16.1	41.2	56.1	43.9
1940	131,669,275	7.2	44.2	56.5	43.5
1950	150,697,361	14.5	50.7	64.0	36.0
1960	179,323,175	18.5	50.6	69.9	30.1
1970	203,302,031	13.4	57.4	73.5	26.5
1980	226,545,805	11.4	64.0	73.7	26.3
1990	248,709,873	9.8	70.2[1]	72.8[2]	27.2[2]

1. Estimated.   2. Figures are for 1989.

Source: John W. Wright (ed.), *The Universal Almanac* (Kansas City: Andrews & McNeel, 1992), p. 200.

Reprinted by permission of Universal Press Syndicate.

3. Now let us explore how a graph helps us to see a set of data in a different light. Then we will return to the two questions just asked.

    a. Select and make a graphical representation for the population data from 1790 to 1990. Describe any problems you had in constructing the graph and how you solved these problems—for example, choosing a scale that would enable you to fit numbers as low as 3 million and as high as 250 million.

    b. Does the graph help you to see the population growth in a different light? If so, briefly explain.

c. Compare and discuss graphs with your partner(s). If you wish to make any changes in your graph as a result of this discussion, note the changes and the reason for making the changes.

d. Now predict the population in the year 2000 based on your impressions of the graph. Briefly describe how you obtained the number. Compare this number to your prediction in Step 2(b). Compare numbers with your partner(s).

4. Now let us examine how graphs can enrich our understanding of the growth in population.

a. Make two line graphs, the first graph showing the actual increase in population from decade to decade and the second graph showing the percent increase in population from decade to decade.

b. The first of these graphs shows population growth from an additive perspective, the second, from a multiplicative perspective. Describe the different impressions that each graph gives. Summarize the advantages and disadvantages of displaying the population increase in each of these ways.

c. Describe the growth of the U.S. population over the last 50 years. Then compare your response to the one you gave in 2(a).

Population Density

5. **a.** Focus now on the "Pop. per sq. mi." column. Describe your first impressions and any questions about the data.

b. Suppose someone came up to you and said, "I don't see the point of these numbers; what do they tell you, anyway?" How would you respond to that person?

6. Look at the data from the table called "Resident Population—States: 1970 to 1992," on page 152 which shows the population density of each state.

a. Select the appropriate data and make a graph that gives a sense of the population density of the 50 states.

b. Compare and discuss graphs with your partner(s). If you wish to make any changes in your graph as a result of this discussion, note the changes and the reason for making the changes.

No. 31. Resident Population—States: 1970 to 1992

[As of July 1, except 1970, 1980, and 1990, as of April 1. Insofar as possible, population shown for all years is that of present area of State; for area figures of States, see table 355. Minus sign (−) indicates decrease. See *Historical Statistics, Colonial Times to 1970*, series A 172, for population by regions, and A 195-198 for population and density, by States]

REGION, DIVISION AND STATE	POPULATION (1,000) 1970	1980[1]	1984	1985	1986	1987	1988	1989	1990	1991	1992	RANK 1970	1980	1990	1992	PCT CHG 1970–80	1980–90	1990–92	POP/SQ MI[2] 1970	1980	1990	1992
U.S.	203,302	226,546	235,825	237,924	240,133	242,289	244,499	246,819	248,710	252,160	255,082	(X)	(X)	(X)	(X)	11.4	9.8	2.6	57.5	64.1	70.3	72.1
Northeast	49,061	49,135	49,718	49,869	50,071	50,302	50,584	50,757	50,809	50,961	51,118	(X)	(X)	(X)	(X)	0.2	3.4	0.6	302.3	302.8	313.1	315.0
N.E.	11,848	12,348	12,642	12,741	12,833	12,951	13,085	13,182	13,207	13,195	13,200	(X)	(X)	(X)	(X)	4.2	7.0	—	188.6	196.6	210.3	210.2
ME	994	1,125	1,156	1,163	1,170	1,185	1,204	1,220	1,228	1,234	1,235	38	38	40	39	13.2	9.2	0.6	32.2	36.5	39.8	40.0
NH	738	921	977	997	1,025	1,054	1,083	1,105	1,109	1,104	1,111	41	42	40	41	24.8	20.5	0.1	82.2	102.6	123.7	123.8
VT	445	511	527	530	534	540	550	558	563	567	570	48	48	48	49	15.0	10.0	1.2	48.1	55.3	60.8	61.6
MA	5,689	5,737	5,841	5,881	5,903	5,935	5,980	6,015	6,018	5,998	5,998	10	11	13	13	0.8	4.9	−0.3	725.8	732.0	767.6	765.3
RI	950	947	962	969	977	990	996	1,001	1,003	1,005	1,005	39	40	43	43	−0.3	5.9	0.2	908.8	906.4	960.3	961.8
CT	3,032	3,108	3,180	3,201	3,224	3,247	3,272	3,283	3,287	3,289	3,281	24	25	27	27	2.5	5.8	−0.2	625.8	641.4	678.5	677.2
M.A.	37,213	36,787	37,076	37,128	37,238	37,350	37,499	37,575	37,602	37,766	37,918	(X)	(X)	(X)	(X)	−1.1	2.2	0.8	374.1	369.9	378.0	381.0
NY	18,241	17,558	17,746	17,792	17,833	17,869	17,941	17,983	17,990	18,055	18,119	2	2	2	2	−3.7	2.5	0.7	386.3	371.8	381.0	383.7
NJ	7,171	7,365	7,515	7,566	7,622	7,671	7,712	7,726	7,730	7,753	7,789	8	9	9	9	2.7	5.0	0.8	966.6	992.7	1,041.9	1,049.9
PA	11,801	11,864	11,815	11,771	11,783	11,811	11,846	11,866	11,882	11,958	12,009	3	4	5	5	0.5	0.1	1.1	263.3	264.7	265.1	267.9
Midwest	56,589	58,866	58,775	58,820	58,848	59,018	59,254	59,468	59,669	60,239	60,713	(X)	(X)	(X)	(X)	4.0	1.4	1.8	75.3	78.3	79.4	80.8
E.N.C.	40,262	41,682	41,393	41,418	41,455	41,590	41,721	41,873	42,009	42,427	42,753	(X)	(X)	(X)	(X)	3.5	0.8	1.8	165.3	171.2	172.5	175.5
OH	10,657	10,798	10,738	10,735	10,730	10,760	10,799	10,829	10,847	10,941	11,016	6	6	7	7	1.3	0.5	1.6	260.2	263.7	264.9	269.0
IN	5,195	5,490	5,458	5,459	5,454	5,473	5,492	5,524	5,544	5,610	5,662	11	12	14	14	5.7	1.0	2.1	144.8	153.1	154.6	157.8
IL	11,110	11,427	11,411	11,400	11,387	11,391	11,390	11,410	11,430	11,543	11,631	5	5	6	6	2.8	(Z)	1.8	199.9	205.6	205.6	209.2
MI	8,882	9,262	9,049	9,076	9,128	9,187	9,218	9,253	9,295	9,380	9,437	7	8	8	8	4.3	0.4	1.5	156.3	163.0	163.6	166.1
WI	4,418	4,706	4,736	4,748	4,756	4,778	4,822	4,857	4,892	4,956	5,007	16	16	16	18	6.5	4.0	2.3	81.3	86.6	90.1	92.2
W.N.C.	16,327	17,183	17,382	17,402	17,393	17,402	17,533	17,595	17,660	17,812	17,960	(X)	(X)	(X)	(X)	5.2	2.8	1.7	32.1	33.8	34.8	35.4
MN	3,806	4,076	4,158	4,184	4,205	4,235	4,296	4,338	4,375	4,432	4,480	19	21	20	20	7.1	7.3	2.4	47.8	51.2	55.0	56.3
IA	2,825	2,914	2,859	2,830	2,792	2,767	2,768	2,771	2,777	2,795	2,812	25	27	30	30	3.1	−4.7	1.3	50.6	52.1	49.7	50.3
MO	4,678	4,917	4,975	5,000	5,023	5,057	5,082	5,096	5,117	5,117	5,193	13	15	15	15	5.1	4.1	1.5	67.9	71.4	74.3	75.4
ND	618	653	680	677	669	661	655	646	639	635	636	45	46	47	47	5.7	−2.1	−0.5	9.0	9.5	9.3	9.2
SD	666	691	697	698	696	696	698	697	696	704	711	44	45	45	45	3.7	0.8	2.2	8.8	9.1	9.2	9.4
NE	1,485	1,570	1,589	1,585	1,574	1,567	1,571	1,575	1,578	1,593	1,606	35	35	36	36	5.7	0.5	1.7	19.3	20.4	20.5	20.9
KS	2,249	2,364	2,424	2,427	2,433	2,445	2,462	2,473	2,478	2,495	2,523	28	32	32	32	5.1	4.8	1.8	27.5	28.9	30.3	30.8
South	62,812	75,372	80,417	81,049	82,328	83,208	83,890	84,700	85,446	86,903	88,143	(X)	(X)	(X)	(X)	20.0	13.4	3.2	72.1	86.5	98.1	101.2
S.A.	30,678	36,959	39,492	40,159	40,863	41,619	42,318	43,008	43,567	44,403	45,061	(X)	(X)	(X)	(X)	20.5	17.9	3.4	115.2	138.8	163.6	169.3
DE	548	594	612	618	628	637	648	658	666	680	689	46	47	46	46	8.4	12.1	3.5	280.4	304.0	340.8	352.5
MD	3,924	4,217	4,365	4,413	4,487	4,566	4,658	4,727	4,781	4,859	4,908	18	19	19	19	7.5	13.4	2.7	401.4	431.4	489.2	502.1
DC	757	638	633	635	638	637	630	624	607	595	589	18	17	17	17	−15.6	−4.9	−3.0	12,404.4	10,466.1	9,649.2	9,649.5
VA	4,651	5,347	5,644	5,715	5,812	5,932	6,037	6,120	6,187	6,280	6,377	14	14	12	12	14.9	15.7	3.1	117.5	135.0	156.3	161.0
WV	1,744	1,950	1,928	1,907	1,882	1,858	1,830	1,807	1,793	1,803	1,812	34	34	34	35	11.8	−8.0	1.0	72.4	81.0	74.5	75.2
NC	5,084	5,882	6,164	6,254	6,322	6,404	6,481	6,565	6,629	6,736	6,843	12	10	10	10	15.7	12.7	3.2	104.4	120.7	136.1	140.5
SC	2,591	3,122	3,272	3,303	3,343	3,381	3,412	3,457	3,487	3,560	3,603	26	24	25	25	20.5	11.7	3.3	86.0	103.6	115.8	119.7
GA	4,588	5,463	5,835	5,963	6,085	6,208	6,316	6,411	6,478	6,623	6,751	15	13	11	11	19.1	18.6	4.2	79.2	94.3	111.8	116.6
FL	6,791	9,746	11,040	11,351	11,668	11,997	12,306	12,638	12,938	13,266	13,488	9	7	4	4	43.5	32.7	4.2	125.8	180.5	239.6	249.8
E.S.C.	12,808	14,666	14,912	14,971	15,012	15,070	15,107	15,136	15,176	15,350	15,529	(X)	(X)	(X)	(X)	14.5	3.5	2.3	71.7	82.1	85.0	86.9
KY	3,221	3,661	3,695	3,695	3,688	3,683	3,680	3,677	3,685	3,713	3,755	23	23	23	24	13.7	0.7	1.9	81.1	92.1	92.8	94.5
TN	3,926	4,591	4,687	4,715	4,739	4,783	4,822	4,854	4,877	4,953	5,024	17	17	17	17	16.9	6.2	3.0	95.2	111.4	118.3	121.9
AL	3,444	3,894	3,952	3,973	3,992	4,015	4,024	4,030	4,041	4,091	4,136	21	22	22	22	13.1	3.8	2.4	67.9	76.7	79.6	81.5
MS	2,217	2,521	2,578	2,588	2,594	2,589	2,580	2,574	2,573	2,593	2,614	29	31	31	31	13.7	2.1	1.6	47.3	53.7	54.8	55.7
W.S.C.	19,326	23,747	26,013	26,279	26,453	26,518	26,466	26,556	26,703	27,151	27,554	(X)	(X)	(X)	(X)	22.9	12.4	3.2	45.3	55.7	62.6	64.6
AR	1,923	2,286	2,320	2,327	2,332	2,342	2,343	2,346	2,351	2,373	2,399	32	33	33	33	18.9	2.8	2.0	36.9	43.9	45.1	46.1
LA	3,645	4,206	4,400	4,408	4,407	4,344	4,289	4,253	4,220	4,254	4,287	20	19	21	21	15.4	0.3	1.6	83.7	96.5	96.9	98.4
OK	2,559	3,025	3,286	3,271	3,253	3,210	3,167	3,150	3,146	3,175	3,212	27	26	28	28	18.2	4.0	2.1	37.3	44.1	45.8	46.8
TX	11,199	14,229	16,007	16,273	16,561	16,622	16,667	16,807	16,987	17,348	17,656	4	3	3	3	27.1	19.4	3.9	42.8	54.3	64.9	67.4
West	34,838	43,172	46,914	47,827	48,786	49,762	50,770	51,894	52,786	54,056	55,108	(X)	(X)	(X)	(X)	23.9	22.3	4.4	19.9	24.6	30.1	31.5
Mt.	8,289	11,373	12,518	12,741	12,952	13,145	13,303	13,498	13,659	14,036	14,381	(X)	(X)	(X)	(X)	37.2	20.1	5.3	9.7	13.3	16.0	16.8
MT	694	787	821	822	814	805	800	800	799	809	824	43	44	44	44	13.3	1.6	3.1	4.8	5.4	5.5	5.7
ID	713	944	991	994	990	985	986	994	1,007	1,040	1,067	42	41	42	42	32.4	6.7	6.0	8.6	11.4	12.2	12.9
WY	332	470	505	500	496	477	465	458	454	460	466	49	49	50	50	41.3	−3.4	2.8	3.4	4.8	4.7	4.8
CO	2,210	2,890	3,170	3,209	3,237	3,260	3,262	3,276	3,294	3,378	3,470	30	28	26	26	30.8	14.0	5.3	21.3	27.9	31.8	33.5
NM	1,017	1,303	1,417	1,438	1,463	1,479	1,490	1,504	1,515	1,549	1,581	37	37	37	37	28.1	16.3	4.4	8.4	10.7	12.5	13.0
AZ	1,775	2,718	3,067	3,184	3,308	3,437	3,535	3,622	3,665	3,748	3,832	33	29	24	23	53.1	34.8	4.6	15.6	23.9	32.3	33.7
UT	1,059	1,461	1,622	1,643	1,663	1,678	1,706	1,706	1,723	1,770	1,813	36	36	35	34	37.9	17.9	5.2	12.9	17.8	21.0	22.1
NV	489	800	925	951	981	1,023	1,075	1,137	1,202	1,283	1,327	47	43	39	38	63.8	50.1	10.4	4.5	7.3	10.9	12.1
Pac.	26,549	31,800	34,396	35,086	35,835	36,617	37,467	38,397	39,127	40,020	40,726	(X)	(X)	(X)	(X)	19.8	23.0	4.1	29.7	35.5	43.7	45.5
WA	3,413	4,132	4,344	4,400	4,453	4,532	4,640	4,746	4,867	5,012	5,136	22	20	18	16	21.1	17.8	5.5	51.3	62.1	73.1	77.1
OR	2,092	2,633	2,673	2,673	2,684	2,701	2,741	2,791	2,842	2,922	2,977	31	30	29	29	25.9	7.9	4.7	21.8	27.4	29.6	31.0
CA	19,971	23,668	25,844	26,441	27,102	27,777	28,464	29,218	29,760	30,380	30,867	1	1	1	1	18.5	25.7	3.7	128.0	151.7	190.8	197.9
AK	303	402	514	532	544	539	542	547	550	570	587	50	50	49	48	32.8	36.9	6.7	0.5	0.7	1.0	1.0
HI	770	965	1,028	1,040	1,052	1,068	1,080	1,095	1,108	1,137	1,160	40	39	41	40	25.3	14.9	4.6	119.9	150.2	172.5	180.5

    c. Did you learn anything from seeing different graphs or hearing others' impressions?

    d. How do you think the Census Bureau came up with the number 70.2 in the initial set of data? In other words, what mathematics do you think it used?

Area of Residence

7. Now look at the "Percent urban" and "Percent rural" columns from the initial table on page 150.

    a. Describe your first impressions and any questions you have about the data.

    b. Select and make a graph that gives a sense of the increasing urbanization of the United States.

    c. Compare and discuss graphs with your partner(s). If you wish to make any changes in your graph as a result of this discussion, note the changes and the reason for making the changes.

    d. Describe something you learned from seeing different graphs or hearing others' impressions.

EXPLORATION 7.2 **Population Change**

Part 1: Changes in where we are

1. Look again at the table entitled "Resident Population—States: 1970 to 1992."

    a. Make a bar graph comparing the populations of the four major regions of the country in 1980 and 1990.

    b. Summarize your impressions.

    c. Now make a bar graph comparing the percent change for each of the regions.

    d. Summarize your impressions.

e. Compare and contrast the two graphs with respect to what they tell us about the changes in population in these regions.

2. When we look at the population change data for all 50 states, it is easy to become overwhelmed by the data. Let us examine a graph to give us a sense of relative population change. At the end of the book you will find a blank map of the United States. You will select several categories and a color-coding scheme. That is, those states whose population declined might be shaded in red, those whose population increased "only a bit" might be left white, and those whose population increased "a lot" might be shaded in gray. There is no "right" number of categories, although 2 is probably too few and 10 is clearly too many.

a. Discuss with members of your group the categories you will select and then color in the map accordingly.

b. Describe what you see from this graph that you didn't see from the numbers alone.

c. Present your graph to the class and listen to the other groups' presentations. Summarize what you learned from the other presentations.

d. There are two very different ways to "see" the population change. Let us examine them in terms of two students. Discuss the relative pros and cons of each perspective.

Anno made the following categories:

A = states whose population decreased

B = states whose population increase was between 1 and 2 million

C = states whose population increase was between 2 million and 4 million

D = states whose population increase was between 4 million and 6 million

E = states whose population increase was more than 6 million

Jasmine made the following categories:

A = states whose population decreased

B = states whose population increase was less than 10%

C = states whose population increase was between 10% and 20%

D = states whose population increase was between 20% and 30%

E = states whose population increase was more than 30%

Part 2: Changes in who we are

1. Look at the "Ancestry of U.S. Population by Rank" table on page 55.

a. Describe your first impressions and any questions about the data.

b. Brainstorm the kinds of graphs that might illustrate these data.

c. If you were to make a graph to visually display (some of) these numbers, describe the graph you would make and justify your choice. This at least involves making a case for the advantages of that graph and may involve explaining why you chose it over other graphs.

Ancestry of U.S. Population by Rank, 1990 Census

1990 Rank	Ancestry group	Number	Percent	1990 Rank	Ancestry group	Number	Percent
	Total population	248,709,873	100.0	33	Japanese	1,004,645	0.4
1	German	57,947,873	23.3	34	Austrian	864,783	0.3
2	Irish	38,735,539	15.6	35	Cuban	859,739	0.3
3	English	32,651,788	13.1	36	Korean	836,987	0.3
4	Afro American	23,777,098	9.6	37	Lithuanian	811,865	0.3
5	Italian	14,664,550	5.9	38	Ukrainian	740,803	0.3
6	American	12,395,999	5.0	39	Scandinavian	678,880	0.3
7	Mexican	11,586,983	4.7	40	Acadian/Cajun	668,271	0.3
8	French	10,320,935	4.1	41	Finnish	658,870	0.3
9	Polish	9,366,106	3.8	42	United States	643,561	0.3
10	American Indian	8,708,220	3.5	43	Asian Indian	570,322	0.2
11	Dutch	6,227,089	2.5	44	Canadian	549,990	0.2
12	Scotch-Irish	5,617,773	2.3	45	Croatian	544,270	0.2
13	Scottish	5,393,581	2.2	46	Vietnamese	535,825	0.2
14	Swedish	4,680,863	1.9	47	Dominican	505,690	0.2
15	Norwegian	3,869,395	1.6	48	Salvadoran	499,153	0.2
16	Russian	2,952,987	1.2	49	European	466,718	0.2
17	French Canadian	2,167,127	0.9	50	Jamaican	435,024	0.2
18	Welsh	2,033,893	0.8	51	Lebanese	394,180	0.2
19	Spanish	2,024,004	0.8	52	Belgian	380,498	0.2
20	Puerto Rican	1,955,323	0.8	53	Romanian	365,544	0.1
21	Slovak	1,882,897	0.8	54	Spaniard	360,935	0.1
22	White	1,799,711	0.7	55	Colombian	351,717	0.1
23	Danish	1,634,669	0.7	56	Czechoslovakian	315,285	0.1
24	Hungarian	1,582,302	0.6	57	Armenian	308,096	0.1
25	Chinese	1,505,245	0.6	58	Pennsylvania German	305,841	0.1
26	Filipino	1,450,512	0.6	59	Haitian	289,521	0.1
27	Czech	1,296,411	0.5	60	Yugoslavian	257,994	0.1
28	Portuguese	1,153,351	0.5	61	Hawaiian	256,081	0.1
29	British	1,119,154	0.4	62	African	245,845	0.1
30	Hispanic	1,113,259	0.4	63	Guatemalan	241,559	0.1
31	Greek	1,110,373	0.4	64	Iranian	235,521	0.1
32	Swiss	1,045,495	0.4	65	Ecuadorian	197,374	0.1

Source: *Information Please Almanac* (Boston: Houghton Mifflin, 1994), p. 836. Source of data: Department of Commerce, U.S. Bureau of the Census. Reprinted from The 1994 Information Please Almanac © 1993 by INSO Corporation.

2. Look at the "Immigrants to U.S. by Country of Origin" table of data on page 156.

a. Describe your first impressions and any questions about the data.

b. Let us focus on a specific subset of the data, that is, how the relative proportions of immigrants from 1951 to 1960 are similar to and different from the relative proportions of immigrants from 1981 to 1990. Even now there is too much data for a clear graph, so we will focus on the following categories: Europe, Asia, Canada and Newfoundland, Latin America, Africa, and "Other." Obtain the numbers for these six categories now.

Immigrants to U.S. by Country of Origin

(Figures are totals, not annual averages, and were tabulated as follows: 1820–67, alien passengers arrived; 1868–91 and 1895–97, immigrant aliens arrived; 1892–94 and 1898 to present, immigrant aliens admitted. 1989 and 1990 totals include legalized immigrants. (Data before 1906 relate to country whence alien came; 1906–80, to country of last permanent residence; 1981 to present data based on country of birth.)

Countries	1992	1820–1992	1981–90	1971–80	1961–70	1951–60	1941–50	1820–1940
Europe: Albania[1]	682	3,914	479	329	98	59	85	2,040
Austria[2]	701	2,662,608	4,636	9,478	20,621	67,106	24,860	2,534,617
Belgium	780	210,501	5,706	5,329	9,192	18,575	12,189	158,205
Bulgaria[3]	1,049	72,156	2,342	1,188	619	104	375	65,856
Czechoslovakia[1]	1,181	152,411	11,500	6,023	3,273	918	8,347	120,013
Denmark	764	371,787	5,380	4,439	9,201	10,984	5,393	335,025
Estonia[1]	194	1,511	137	91	163	185	212	506
Finland[1]	525	38,222	3,265	2,868	4,192	4,925	2,503	19,593
France	3,288	784,096	23,124	25,069	45,237	51,121	38,809	594,998
Germany[2]	9,888	7,078,012	70,111	74,414	190,796	477,765	226,578	6,021,951
Great Britian	19,973	5,135,957	142,123	137,374	213,822	202,824	139,306	4,266,561
Greece	1,858	698,594	29,130	92,369	85,969	47,608	8,973	430,608
Hungary[2]	1,304	1,673,817	9,764	6,550	5,401	36,637	3,469	1,609,158
Ireland	12,226	4,742,999	32,823	11,490	32,966	48,362	14,789	4,580,557
Italy	2,592	5,343,689	32,894	129,368	214,111	185,491	57,661	4,719,223
Latvia[1]	419	3,486	359	207	510	352	361	1,192
Lithuania[1]	353	4,928	482	248	562	242	683	2,201
Luxembourg[1]	25	3,214	234	307	556	684	820	565
Netherlands	1,586	376,821	11,958	10,492	30,606	52,277	14,860	253,759
Norway[4]	665	754,607	3,901	3,941	15,484	22,935	10,100	697,095
Poland[5]	25,504	665,177	97,390	37,234	53,539	9,985	7,571	414,755
Portugal	2,748	508,122	40,020	101,710	76,065	19,588	7,423	256,044
Romania[6]	6,500	227,543	39,963	12,393	2,531	1,039	1,076	156,945
Spain	1,631	283,893	15,698	39,141	44,659	7,894	2,898	170,123
Sweden[4]	1,463	1,393,971	10,211	6,531	17,116	21,697	10,665	1,325,208
Switzerland	1,023	359,385	7,076	8,235	18,453	17,675	10,547	295,680
Former U.S.S.R.[7]	43,614	3,570,704	84,081	38,961	2,465	671	571	3,343,361
Former Yugoslavia[3]	2,604	142,008	19,182	30,540	20,381	8,225	1,576	56,787
Other Europe	252	61,383	2,661	4,049	4,904	9,799	3,447	36,060
Total Europe	145,392	37,325,766	705,630	800,368	1,123,492	1,325,727	621,147	32,468,776
Asia: China[8]	38,907	1,028,247	388,686	124,326	34,764	9,657	16,709	382,173
India	36,755	548,690	261,841	164,134	27,189	1,973	1,761	9,873
Israel	5,104	138,905	36,353	37,713	29,602	25,476	476	—
Japan[9]	11,028	474,484	43,248	49,775	39,988	46,250	1,555	277,591
Turkey	2,488	414,953	20,843	13,399	10,142	3,519	798	361,236
Other Asia	262,673	4,208,748	2,042,025	1,198,831	285,957	66,374	15,729	44,053
Total Asia[10]	356,955	6,813,937	2,066,455	1,588,178	427,642	153,249	37,028	1,074,926
America: Canada and Newfoundland[11]	15,205	4,286,560	119,204	169,939	413,310	377,952	171,718	3,005,728
Central America	57,558	979,044	458,753	134,640	101,330	44,751	21,665	49,154
Mexico[12]	213,802	5,046,105	1,653,250	640,294	453,937	299,811	60,589	778,255
South America	55,308	1,379,675	455,977	295,741	257,954	91,628	21,831	121,302
West Indies	94,806	2,955,159	892,392	741,126	470,213	123,091	49,725	446,971
Other America[12]	2,676	117,078	1,352	995	19,630	59,711	29,276	56
Total America	439,355	14,763,521	3,580,928	1,982,735	1,716,374	996,944	354,804	4,401,466
Africa	27,086	412,729	192,212	80,779	28,954	14,092	7,367	26,060
Australia and New Zealand	3,205	149,303	20,169	23,788	19,562	11,506	13,805	54,437
Pacific Islands[13]	89	57,664	21,041	17,454	5,560	1,470	746	11,089
Countries not specified[14]	1,895	272,238	196	12	93	12,491	142	253,689
Total all countries	973,977	59,795,158	7,338,062	4,493,314	3,321,677	2,515,479	1,035,039	38,290,443

1. Countries established since beginning of World War I are included with countries to which they belonged. 2. Data for Austria-Hungary not reported until 1861. Austria and Hungary recorded separately after 1905, Austria included with Germany 1938–45. 3. Bulgaria, Serbia, Montenegro first reported in 1899. Bulgaria reported separately since 1920. In 1920, separate enumeration for Kingdom of Serbs, Croats, Slovenes; since 1922, recorded as Yugoslavia. 4. Norway included with Sweden 1820–68. 5. Included with Austria-Hungary, Germany, and Russia 1899–1919. 6. No record of immigration until 1880. 7. From 1931–63, the U.S.S.R. was broken down into European U.S.S.R. and Asian U.S.S.R. Since 1964, total U.S.S.R. has been reported in Europe. 8. Beginning in 1957, China includes Taiwan. 9. No record of immigration until 1861. 10. From 1934, Asia included Philippines; before 1934, recorded in separate tables as insular travel. 11. Includes all British North American possessions, 1820–98. 12. No record of immigration, 1886–93. 13. Included with "Countries not specified" prior to 1925. 14. Includes 32,897 persons returning in 1906 to their homes in U.S. *Source of data:* Department of Justice, Immigration and Naturalization Service. NOTE: Data are latest available. Source: *Information Please Almanac* (Boston: Houghton Mifflin, 1994), pp. 28–29.

c. What can you say about changes in immigration just from seeing these numbers? Imagine that you were writing an article about changes in immigration patterns for a newspaper. What would you write?

d. Now divide your group in half. One half of the group will make a bar graph for these data, and the other half will make a circle graph. After making the graphs, present them to the group and describe what the graphs tell us that the numbers alone do not.

e. If you were to select one of the graphs to include in the newspaper article, which would it be? Justify your choice.

Part 3: Changes in How Old We Are

Look at the data below.

Population Distribution by Age, Race, Nativity, and Sex

| | | | | Age | | | | Race and Nativity | | | |
| | | | | | | | | White | | | |
Year	Total	Under 5	5–19	20–44	45–64	65 and over	Total	Native born	Foreign born	Black	Other races[2]
PERCENT DISTRIBUTION											
1860	100.0	15.4	35.8	35.7	10.4	2.7	85.6	72.6	13.0	14.1	0.3
1870	100.0	14.3	35.4	35.4	11.9	3.0	87.1	72.9	14.2	12.7	0.2
1880	100.0	13.8	34.3	35.9	12.6	3.4	86.5	73.4	13.1	13.1	0.3
1890	100.0	12.2	33.9	36.9	13.1	3.9	87.5	73.0	14.5	11.9	0.3
1900	100.0	12.1	32.3	37.7	13.7	4.1	87.9	74.5	13.4	11.6	0.5
1910	100.0	11.6	30.4	39.0	14.6	4.3	88.9	74.4	14.5	10.7	0.4
1920	100.0	10.9	29.8	38.4	16.1	4.7	89.7	76.7	13.0	9.9	0.4
1930	100.0	9.3	29.5	38.3	17.4	5.4	89.8	78.4	11.4	9.7	0.5
1940	100.0	8.0	26.4	38.9	19.8	6.8	89.8	81.1	8.7	9.8	0.4
1950	100.0	10.7	23.2	37.6	20.3	8.1	89.5	82.8	6.7	10.0	0.5
1960	100.0	11.3	27.1	32.2	20.1	9.2	88.6	83.4	5.2	10.5	0.9
1970	100.0	8.4	29.5	31.7	20.6	9.8	87.6	83.4	4.3	11.1	1.4
1980	100.0	7.2	24.8	37.1	19.6	11.3	83.1	n.a.	n.a.	11.7	5.2
1990	100.0	7.6	21.3	40.1	18.6	12.5	83.9	n.a.	n.a.	12.3	3.8

Source: *Information Please* (Boston: Houghton Mifflin, 1994), p. 829. Source of data: Department of Commerce, U.S. Bureau of the Census. Reprinted from The 1994 Information Please Almanac © 1993 by INSO Corporation.

1. Describe your first impressions and any questions about the data.

2. **a.** Now let us focus on understanding the phenomenon that is called "the aging of the United States." First, describe what you know about this phenomenon and why it is a concern.

b. Brainstorm the kinds of graphs that might illustrate these data — that is, illustrate the changes in the proportions of the population that are of different ages: under 5, 5–19, 20–44, 45–64, and 65 and over.

c. Let us now focus on three years: 1900, 1950, and 1990. Select a way to represent these data graphically. Then make the graph(s) and justify your choice.

d. Compare your graph(s) with other students. Note any insights from the discussion.

e. Write a short paragraph describing the aging of the population that would accompany your graph from Step 2(d).

Looking Back

1. Describe your most important mathematical learning(s) as a result of Explorations 7.1 and 7.2.

2. Describe one or two things that you learned about the United States from these explorations.

3. Did these explorations make you curious about other aspects of the U.S. population? Go to an almanac or abstract to find data that might answer your questions about these other aspects of population. Select one group of data and present those data and one graphical display of the data. This report needs to include the following:

a. The data and your first impressions of the data.

b. Questions you have about the data, concerning reliability, validity, or numbers or sentences that you don't understand.

c. Your graph, your justification of your choice of that graph, and a verbal summary of the graph, as if in a newspaper article accompanying the graph.

d. Your two most important learnings from examining the data and making the graph.

SECTION 7.2   **EXPLORING DISTRIBUTIONS:**
CENTERS AND SPREADS

We encounter the concept of "average" frequently in our daily lives. We may think of average in nonmathematical ways, as meaning "so-so," or "typical." In statistics, average has a specific meaning beyond simply "adding all the numbers and dividing."

The following exploration will make the topic of statistics and related concepts feel more real to you. The NCTM Standards say that "Instruction in statistics should focus on the active involvement of students in the entire process: formulating key questions; collecting and organizing data; representing the data using graphs, tables, frequency distributions, and summary statistics; analyzing the data; making conjectures; and communicating information in a convincing way" (*Curriculum Standards*, p. 105).

EXPLORATION 7.3   **Typical Person**

The word *typical* conjures up many of the same thoughts that the word *average* does. In this exploration, you will develop a profile of the typical person in your class by analyzing data that you and your classmates decide to collect.

1. Briefly describe topics about which you would like to collect data, for example, number of siblings, place of birth, number of schools attended in grades K–12, favorite TV show, and so on.

2. Having selected a topic, come up with the question you will ask your classmates. You want to make sure that the question is clear and that everyone will interpret the question in the same way. For example, if your topic is "number of brothers and sisters," how might others interpret this statement in different ways?

3. Analyze your data.

    a. First, discuss what kind of graph you want to make. Make the graph and briefly describe why you chose this graph over other graphs.

    b. Determine the mean, median, and mode, as appropriate. How did you calculate these figures? Does one seem to be a more appropriate measure of the typical student than the others? Explain.

    c. Describe any problems you had with the data or with making the graph. That is, describe what the problem was and how you solved that problem.

4. Prepare a presentation for the class. Include your question, your results from Step 3, and the words you will say in your presentation.

Looking Back on Exploration 7.3

1. **a.** Describe the strengths of your group presentation.

   b. Decide whether any of the following changes would make your presentation better: improvements in your graph, a different graph, changes in your presentation of your graph, or your determination and/or interpretation of mean, median, and mode.

2. **a.** Select the group presentation that you thought was the "best" one. Describe what was so good about that presentation.

   b. Select a presentation in which the students chose a graph that you did not think was the best choice for those data. Describe the topic and graph. Describe the kind of graph you think would be more appropriate, and explain why.

3. **a.** Describe the most important thing you learned about mathematics from this exploration.

   b. Which data about characteristics of the typical student surprised you the most? Explain.

4. If you were to write a story for the campus newspaper about the typical elementary education major on your campus, how might you collect the data?

EXPLORATION 7.4   **Data Collection**

1. Select and refine a question for which collection of data will provide some "answers." For example, "How much sleep do I get?" can be refined to "What time do I go to bed and what time do I wake up?"

2. Decide how to collect and represent your data.
   a. What data will you collect?

   b. How will you collect and record the data?

c. How precise will your "measurements" be? It will help at this time to look back and see if the data you are collecting and how you are collecting the data will enable you to answer the question(s) you are asking.

d. Think about how you will represent the data. For example, how will you graph them and how will you show measures of center and variation? (*Note:* You don't have to analyze all the data you collect. A student choosing to collect data on her sleep might sum up Step 2 with, "I will make a chart that will have the day, my bedtime, and my waking time. I will round the times to the nearest five minutes."

3. Collect the data.

4. Analyze and represent the data. See suggestions in Step 2(d).

5. Your instructor will give you the format for your report.

EXPLORATION 7.5 **Tailgating**

Most likely, either your parents or your driving instructor warned you about the dangers of tailgating. How do you know whether or not you are too close to the car in front of you? How close is too close? We will use data to address these questions in this exploration.

1. Describe with your partner(s) the guidelines concerning tailgating that you presently use. Do those guidelines make sense? If they do not make sense to you, what is wrong with them?

2. Let's say we wanted to gather information to determine a safe distance between two moving cars. Discuss the problem with your partner(s).

a. Define the question. This includes complexities (for example, we need more distance at higher speeds).

b. Determine the information you will need to obtain (through research) to answer the question.

c. Discuss your ideas with another group. Note any ideas that you got from the group discussion.

3. Let us focus on several key aspects of this question. Discuss how you would measure reaction time. Meet with another group and share ideas.

   a. Design a method for determining reaction time.

   b. Gather the information. Discuss and address issues of precision.

   c. Analyze the information.

   d. Develop your conclusions about reaction time.

   e. Describe questions you still have about determining and communicating how far is a safe distance.

   f. Share your conclusions and questions with other groups.

4. Describe how you can translate your data into recommendations that people can use. For example, if you say that there should be x feet between you and the car ahead of you at 60 miles per hour, you need a way to describe how a person can "measure" x feet while inside the car!

5. Determine your recommended distance between cars at 20 mph, 30 mph, 40 mph, 50 mph, and 60 mph. Are the speeds and recommended distances proportional? How do you know? Should they be?

Looking Back on Exploration 7.5

Describe the most important thing you learned from this exploration.

EXPLORATION 7.6   Making Sense of Pulse Data

This exploration focuses on collecting, analyzing, and comparing two sets of related data. We will collect data on one's resting pulse and one's pulse after two minutes of moderate exercise.

1. **a.** What do you think the average pulse for this class will be?

b. Do you think there is a relationship between pulse and other variables? If so, what do you think this relationship is?

2. In your group, discuss how to take your pulse so that the data will be accurate. For each of the factors, record and justify your decision.

    a. Do we place our fingers on our wrist, heart, or neck? Does it matter?

    b. How long a time period do we use—10 seconds, 15 seconds, 30 seconds, or 1 minute? Does it matter?

    c. How do we report the numbers? For example, if you take the number of beats in 10 seconds, would you use this number or multiply by 6 to get the number of beats per minute? Does it matter?

3. Collect and analyze the data.

    a. Before you collect the data, predict whether you expect the mean, median, and mode to be pretty close or not pretty close (recall Exploration 7.3: Typical Person) and give the reasoning behind your prediction.

    b. Take the pulses of the class members, and write them down.

    c. Determine the mean, median, and mode.

    d. In this case, which one would you select when saying, "The average pulse in our class was _____"? Justify your choice.

4. Now examine what happens to the pulse after moderate exercise.

    a. Before doing the exercise, determine whether you will measure your pulse by counting beats for 10, 15, 20, 30, or 60 seconds. Does it matter?

    b. Also predict whether you expect the variation for this set of data to be less than, equal to, or greater than the variation for the previous set of data.

c. Take the pulses of the class members, and write them down.

d. Determine the mean, median, and mode.

5. Complete the following sentence: "When we compared the effect of moderate exercise on pulse, we found _____"? Justify your response.

6. Let us now examine how we can use graphs to help us compare the two sets of data.
   a. Make a grouped frequency table, a histogram, and a boxplot for both sets of data.

   b. Describe observations you can make from each kind of graph.

   c. If you were to present what you have learned about how pulses change as a result of moderate exercise, which graph would you select? Why?

Looking Back on Exploration 7.6

1. What did you learn from this exploration?

2. What questions do you still have?

3. If you were to continue to investigate pulse rates, what data would you collect next? Why?

S E C T I O N   7.3   **EXPLORING CONCEPTS RELATED TO CHANCE**

Chances are, you have some understanding of probability concepts. For instance, you know that when you roll dice, the probability of getting a 2 is less than the probability of getting a 7. You know that the probability of snow is less in Atlanta than in Buffalo.

Like the concept of "average," "chance" also has a specific meaning that you will explore in this section. In the process, you will use some tools you have developed in earlier chapters and develop some new ones.

E X P L O R A T I O N 7.7   **Using Sampling to Estimate a Whole Population**

Scientists have used the idea of sampling and proportions to estimate various wildlife populations. This exploration is a simulation of a method that has been used by naturalists to estimate the number of fish in a lake.

Your group will obtain a supply of "fish" from your instructor, and you will estimate the total number of fish without counting every single one.

1. Obtain your "fish" from your instructor and place them in a container. The container represents the lake in which these fish are distributed. Imagine that there were concerns that the lake's fish population was declining and that this would hurt tourism, which would in turn hurt the local economy. You have been asked to determine the number of fish in the lake. This number will be used as a baseline, so that, when the procedure is repeated in succeeding years, we will be able to see if the population is actually declining.

    a. Take a few minutes to brainstorm possible ways to estimate the number of fish in the lake by a means other than counting all of them.

    b. Select one of your group's ideas and try it out on the fish your instructor gave you. Briefly write up your group's method, your justification of the method, and an estimate of the number of fish you got when you applied your method.

2. Now we will explore a method that scientists have used. First, they catch a "reasonable" number of fish and then tag and release them. Then they catch another batch of fish; some of these fish will have tags and some will not. We now have enough data to calculate an estimate of the number of fish in the lake.

    a. Discuss this procedure in your group until you understand both how and why it works. You may want to do a trial run (using the problem-solving strategy "act it out") to help you better understand the procedure.

    b. How do you think the scientists determine what "reasonable" is?

3. Now use the procedure with the fish that your instructor gave you.

    a. Decide how many fish to tag and briefly justify your choice. Tag that number of fish.

    b. Determine the size of your sample — that is, how many fish to catch — and briefly justify your choice. Catch the fish and record the number of caught fish that are tagged and the number that are untagged.

    c. Use this information to estimate the total number of fish in the lake.

d. Repeat parts (b) and (c) until you feel that your estimate is "close." Briefly justify why you think your estimate is close. You may want to use a table like the following:

Sample	Number caught	Number caught that were tagged	Estimate of actual population
1			
2			
3			

4. Have a class discussion in which each group presents its estimate, justifies its choice of numbers of fish to tag and to catch again, and explains its degree of confidence that the estimate is close to the actual population. What did you learn from the class discussion?

5. Imagine doing this in a real lake with real fish.

a. Discuss how many fish it would be reasonable to catch and tag. Describe your group's decision and your group's rationale.

b. In real life, what factors might cause the tagged fish not to be randomly distributed in the lake? How might the biologists deal with these issues?

EXPLORATION 7.8   **Predicting Population Characteristics from Sampling**

Your group has received a bag containing at least two kinds of objects. Your goal is to estimate, through sampling, the proportion of each kind of object. For example, if there are some red chips and some blue chips, your task is to estimate the actual proportions of red and blue chips in the whole "population" of your bag.

1. Obtain your bag from your instructor. Discuss how large you want your sample size to be. Describe your choice and the rationale behind your choice.

2. Obtain and record a sample. Determine your estimate of the actual proportions of the different objects in the bag at this point, or say "not enough data." Describe any insights or questions you have. Repeat this process until you feel confident that you can predict the actual proportions. Summarize your data and your reasoning. You might want to use a table like the one below.

Sample number	Sample size	Number of each object			Predicted actual proportion of each object		
		A	**B**	**C**	**A**	**B**	**C**
1							
2							
3							
Totals							

Insights/questions:

3. Meet with another group that had the same objects. Compare your data and your conclusions. Describe any additional insights or questions you have as a result of your discussion.

4. Have a class discussion in which each group presents its estimate and explains its degree of confidence that the estimate is close to the actual proportions. Describe any additional insights or questions you have as a result of the presentations and discussion.

EXPLORATION 7.9 **Pig**

We will play a variation of a famous dice game that many teachers use to help their students learn probability and statistics concepts. The rules of the game are simple: You roll a standard die as many times as you want and add the numbers from each roll. However, if you roll a 1, then you get 0 points for your entire turn. For example, if you roll 6, 6, 3, 4, and 2 (and then stop), your score is 21. However, if you roll 6, 6, 3, 4, 2, and 1, your turn ends and your score is 0. You can see where the name *Pig* comes from! Each game consists of 10 turns. See how many points you can get from 10 turns.

Part 1: Making and testing hypotheses

1. Play the game alone for 5 to 10 minutes to get a sense of what strategies you would like to test. In other words, what do you think will be the best strategy? After this time, take a minute to note your present thinking.

2. Meet with your group and share ideas.

   a. Each group will now select two or more strategies to test. Justify your reasons for selecting these strategies.

   b. Play several games and record the results.

   c. At this point, do you think one of the strategies you are testing is the best strategy, do you think you need more information, or have you come up with a new strategy that you think is even better? Briefly explain your reasoning.

3. After discussing strategies with the whole class, respond to the following questions.

   a. Which of the strategies discussed in class do you think will produce the highest score over time? Why?

   b. How might we gather and analyze data to find the "best" strategy for winning?

Part 2: Gathering and analyzing data

This part of the exploration models many real-life situations in which we do some research on the topic. That is, we are not immediately going to play more games to compare two or more strategies. Instead, we are going to gather and analyze data on two questions:

- On average, how many times can we roll the die before a 1 occurs?
- On average, how many points will we accumulate before a 1 occurs?

1. Discuss your initial predictions for these two questions in your group. Write down and briefly justify your predictions.

2. Discuss how we might collect and record the data on these questions.

3. As a group, take a certain number of turns, but let each turn continue until you roll a 1. Count the number of rolls in each of these turns, not including the roll that turned up the 1. Also, calculate the number of points accumulated in each of these turns before the 1 turned up. Make tables like the ones below to tally your data.

Number of rolls before a 1 occurs	0	1	2	3	4	5	6	7	8	9	10	11	12	13	14	15	etc.
Frequency																	

Accumulated points before a 1 occurs	0	1	2	3	4	5	6	7	8	9	10	11	12	etc.
Frequency														

4. In Step 5, we will record the data from the whole class. However, before we do, predict what the distributions will look like—will they be uniform, normal, bimodal, skewed to the right or left, or random? Explain your reasoning.

5. Now record the data from the whole class in tables like those below, and make two histograms.

Number of rolls before a 1 occurs	0	1	2	3	4	5	6	7	8	9	10	11	12	13	14	15	etc.
Frequency																	

Accumulated points before a 1 occurs	0	1	2	3	4	5	6	7	8	9	10	11	12	etc.
Frequency														

6. The modes are immediately apparent. Before you compute them, predict the means and the medians. Briefly explain your reasoning. Then determine the means and medians.

7. Compare your empirical findings with your prediction in Step 1. If the results are different from your prediction, can you explain the observed average?

8. Now discuss these two sets of data in your group. Does either set of data support your favorite strategy, or do they suggest a new strategy? Briefly explain your reasoning.

Part 3: Comparing different strategies

1. We will compare the following strategies: "stop after 4 rolls," "stop after 5 rolls," and "stop after 6 rolls."

    a. Which one do you think will win? Why?

    b. Decide how you might gather the data most effectively.

    c. Collect the data for 50 games. Which strategy results in the most points after 50 games? If we programmed a computer to play the game, would this strategy result in the most points after 1,000 games — yes, no, or not sure? Explain your choice.

    d. If we look at only those turns in which points were scored — that is, if we put aside the losing rounds, what do you think will be the average score *per turn* for the "stop after 4" strategy, the "stop after 5" strategy, and the "stop after 6" strategy? Explain your reasoning.

2. We will now analyze the data for each of the three strategies.

    a. Make a histogram and compute the mean and standard deviation (use a calculator or computer). Write a short paragraph explaining what the histogram, mean, and standard deviation tell us about the three strategies.

    b. Make a boxplot for each of the three strategies. Write a short paragraph explaining what the boxplot tells us about the three strategies.

    c. Summarize the pros and cons of the two analyses — that is, the histogram, mean, and standard deviation versus the boxplot.

3. Now analyze another strategy.

    a. Predict the histogram, mean, standard deviation, and boxplot for the "stop after 7" strategy.

    b. Collect the data for the "stop after 7" strategy and make the histogram, mean, standard deviation, and boxplot. Discuss the match between your predictions and the results.

Looking Back on Exploration 7.9

1. Describe your biggest learning(s) from this exploration.

2. Describe any questions that arose from this exploration. These can be in the form of inscrutabilities or what-ifs.

EXPLORATION 7.10   **Buffon's Needle**

In the eighteenth century, the French naturalist Comte de Buffon (1707–1788) performed an experiment that is still interesting today.

The question that he investigated was: If a needle is dropped on a floor made of planks (floorboards), what is the probability that the needle will touch or fall across one of the cracks in the floor when the length of the needle is less than the distance between the planks ($l < d$)? He presented this problem at the University of Paris in 1760 as one way of approximating π.

1. Paraphrase Buffon's question in your own words, then write down your ideas for how to simulate this experiment.

2. Your instructor will give you directions for re-creating this experiment with a toothpick and lined paper instead of a needle and a wood floor.

3. Before you perform the experiment, respond to the following questions.

   a. What is your estimate of the probability that the toothpick will land on or touch a line? Explain your reasoning.

   b. How many times should you drop the toothpick in order to be "relatively" close to the actual probability? Explain your reasoning.

4. Now conduct the experiment with your group. Drop the toothpicks onto the paper from a height of about one foot. If any toothpicks miss the paper, drop them on the paper again. Count and record as "hits" the number of toothpicks that touch or cross the lines.

   Do 10 trial runs. Each trial consists of the number of hits out of 10 drops. Record your results in a table like the one at the right.

Trial	Number of hits
1	
2	
3	
4	
5	
6	
7	
8	
9	
10	

5.   What percent of the drops were hits? (This is called the experimental probability.)

6.   In a moment, we will gather the data from all groups. However, before we do that, answer the following question. If we were to make a histogram from 10,000 trials, what do you think the distribution of that data might look like—would it be uniform, normal, bimodal, of constant slope up (or down), random, or something else? Briefly describe your reasoning in picking that distribution.

7.   Collect the data from all the groups in the class. What is the class's experimental probability?

8.   Buffon found that when the length of the needle is half of the distance between the floorboards, the probability of touching or crossing a crack is $1/\pi$, or about 32%.

    a.   Using this information, calculate your approximation of π from the class data.

    b.   Determine the percent error.

9.   Suppose the needles are the same length as the distance between the planks.

    a.   On what percent of the drops do you predict that the needle will hit a line? Explain the reasoning behind your prediction.

    b.   Repeat the experiment with toothpicks that are the same length as the distance between the lines. Write down the results of the experiment.

10.   Design an experiment in which the toothpicks and the distance between the planks have a different ratio.

    a.   Describe your experiment.

    b.   Describe your findings.

    c.   Based on your data, can you make a general statement that will allow us to find the probability of a needle touching or crossing a line that can be applied to any length needle and any distance between the boards? If so, write it down both in words and as a formula.

11. Although this was a probability experiment, you used other mathematics concepts and topics. What were they? How did you use them?

12. Describe your biggest learning from this exploration.

EXPLORATION 7.11   **How Many Boxes Will You Probably Have to Buy?**

Cereal companies often place prizes inside boxes of cereal to attract customers. One of these promotions lends itself nicely to exploration. Many elementary school teachers have done this exploration, in a simpler form, with their students. It certainly captures their attention!

Part 1: Three prizes

Inside specially marked packages of Sugar Sugar cereal, you can get a photograph of one of three sports figures. Many kids will want to have one of each.

1. How many boxes do you think you would have to buy in order to get one of each? Brainstorm this with your partner(s) and write down your thoughts.

2. We will explore a slightly different question: If you were to buy boxes of cereal until you had all three photographs, how many boxes would you have to buy, on average? How can we figure this out? With your group, devise a plan, describe your plan, and justify your plan.

3. We can simulate this problem in many different ways. However, each of the ways requires that we use random samples. We can rephrase this restriction by saying that we want to simulate this problem by *randomizing*. Brainstorm ways to simulate this problem. Then describe and justify your plan.

4. a. Now that you have a plan for simulating the problem, you need to decide on a plan for recording your data. Describe and justify your plan.

b. Meet with another group to share ideas. If this sharing inspires you to make any changes in how you will record your data, write them down.

5.   Record your group's data and conclusions.

6.   Take the data from all the groups and record those data in a chart like the one below. But first, predict the shape of the distribution of the data and explain your prediction.

Number of boxes that had to be bought	3	4	5	6	7	8	9	10	11	12	etc.
Frequency											

7.   Use the data from the whole class.

    a.   Make a histogram and determine the mean and standard deviation. Briefly describe what the histogram and standard deviation tell us about the data.

    b.   Make a boxplot. Briefly summarize what the boxplot tells us about the data.

    c.   Describe the pros and cons of each graph.

8.   From your data, you can answer questions like: What is the probability of getting all 3 photographs after buying 3 boxes of cereal? after buying 4 boxes? and so on. As you discovered, not every group obtains the same probabilities. These probabilities that you have determined are called experimental probabilities; that is, the numbers come from your experimenting. The Law of Large Numbers states what many people conclude from their own common sense: The larger the sample size, the more likely it is that the experimental probability will be accurate. In this situation, we can also determine the theoretical probabilities. For example, the theoretical probability of getting each of the photographs is 1/3, assuming, of course, that the numbers of each of the three photographs are equal and that the company mixes up the boxes well, so that each store is likely to have equal numbers of the three photographs.

a. Take some time now with your partner(s) to determine the theoretical probabilities of getting 3 different photographs after buying 3 boxes.

b. Describe your method and the problem-solving tools that you used. Discuss your method with another group.

c. Now determine the theoretical probabilities of getting 3 different photographs after buying 4 boxes and after buying 5 boxes. I will give an important hint: It is very important to look for patterns in your representation and to be systematic. The object of this part of the exploration is not so much to get the theoretical probabilities as it is to understand the importance of the problem-solving tools of appropriate diagrams, looking for and using patterns, and being systematic.

d. Extrapolate from your work to predict the theoretical probability after 6 boxes. Describe the reasoning that you used to make your prediction.

e. Describe what you learned about problem-solving from this step of the exploration.

9. Compare the theoretical and experimental probabilities for getting 3 different photos after buying 3 boxes, 4 boxes, and 5 boxes. Why aren't they identical? Which do you trust more? Explain your responses.

Part 2: Extensions

1. Repeat this exploration, assuming that Sugar Sugar cereal offers six different photos, rather than three.

2. Here are one group's data for 25 turns for the variation with six photos.

Number of boxes needed to get 6 photos	6	7	8	9	10	11	12	13	14	15	16	17	18	19	20	21	22	23	24	25	26	27	28	29	30
Frequency	0	2	1	2	2	4	2	3	1	1	2	1	2	0	0	0	0	1	0	0	0	0	0	0	1

a. Determine a way to find the mean without adding all 25 numbers and dividing by 25.

b. Using boxplots, determine whether 23 and/or 30 are outliers.

c. Without adding up the remaining 23 numbers, determine the new mean if we threw out the turns of 23 and 30. Explain how you did this.

Looking Back on Exploration 7.11

1. Describe your biggest learning(s) from this exploration.

2. Describe any questions that arose from this exploration. Note these could be in the form of inscrutabilities or what-ifs.

EXPLORATION 7.12   More Simulations

The following situations present real-life questions for which determining the theoretical probability is either tedious or impossible. Thus, they lend themselves to simulations in which we can determine the experimental probability.

For each of the following questions, develop and execute a simulation plan to help you answer the question. Your instructor will provide the format for your reports.

1. *The basketball game is on the line*   Horace has just been fouled, and there is no time on the clock. His team is down by one point, and he gets two shots. Horace is an 80% free-throw shooter. What percent chance of winning in regulation time does his team have?

2. *Genetics*   Maggie and Tony have just discovered that they are carriers of a genetically transmitted disease, and that they have a 25% chance of passing on this disease to their children. They had planned to have 4 children. If they still have 4 children, what is the probability that at least one of the children will get the disease?

3. *Overbooking*   Airlines commonly overbook; that is, they sell more tickets for a flight than there are seats.

a. Why do you think airlines overbook?

b. An airline has a plane with 40 seats. What information will help it to decide how much to overbook?

c. Using the information from your instructor, develop a simulation plan to help the airline decide how many tickets to sell. Meet with another group to share ideas. Note any changes in your plan.

d. Do the simulation. What is your conclusion? Support your conclusion.

4. *Having children*   In an attempt to deal with overpopulation, the Chinese government has a policy that couples may have only one child. One of the biggest problems with this policy is that in Chinese culture, having a boy is preferable. As a result of the policy and the preference for boys, infanticide is not uncommon in China (and in other countries too — for example, in parts of Nepal, where I was in the Peace Corps). That is, it is not uncommon for parents to kill their newborn baby if it is a girl. Obviously there are many ways to deal with this problem.

a. One way would be to modify the policy to say that a couple could keep having children until they got a boy. However, one mathematical problem with this policy is that it would affect the ratio of men to women. With your partner(s), discuss how this policy would affect the ratio of boys to girls (assuming that there is a 50% chance of having a boy or a girl). Explain, as if you were talking to someone who does not understand, how this policy would affect the ratio.

b. Assume that this policy was implemented. Develop and run a simulation to determine the ratio of boys to girls after the implementation. That is, theoretically, the ratio of boys to girls will be 1:1. If this policy were implemented, what would be the ratio of boys to girls who were born after the implementation?

SECTION   7.4   EXPLORING COUNTING AND CHANCE

Many real-life questions or problems fall into the field of probability called combinatorics. That is, there are patterns that enable us to determine the number of elements in the sample space and the number of elements in the subset in which we are interested.

EXPLORATION 7.13   Area Codes and Phone Numbers

Earlier in this decade, the telephone companies had to address a serious problem: The United States was running out of area codes. You have the tools at your disposal to determine both the cause of the problem and its solution.

1.   What is the theoretical maximum number of phone numbers within an area code? Summarize your work so that the reader can understand how you determined the answer.

2.   As you probably realized in Step 1, there are certain phone numbers that are not allowed. Thus, we need to find out what is the actual maximum number of phone numbers within an area code. Summarize your work so that the reader can understand how you determined the answer.

3.   Look at the area codes from a 1993 phone book. We know that theoretically there are 1,000 possible area codes. Why is this? Since the actual number of area codes is much less than 1,000, there must be some limitations on area codes, just as there are on phone numbers.

    a.   Determine the set of possible area codes in 1993. State your answer as succinctly as possible—that is, by a means other than just listing all of them.

    b.   Describe the set of rules for creating a valid area code number—for example, the second digit must be a 0 or a 1.

4.   If we multiply the number of possible area codes by the number of phone numbers within an area code, we get a number far greater than 250 million. Explain why we still needed more area codes in 1993 despite this fact.

5.   Devise, explain, and justify a plan for solving this problem.

6.   Find out and describe what the solution was to the problem of not enough area codes.

7.   Predict the population of the United States when we will again run out of area codes.

EXPLORATION 7.14   **License Plates**

Some of the readers of this book will have grandparents who can remember life without the automobile, something most of us cannot imagine.

When cars first started being sold, there were no license plates and no driver's licenses. If you could afford a car, you could drive it! However, as cars became more popular, the need to require people to register their cars arose. Police could thus identify cars that were not registered and could identify cars that were being driven unsafely.

The evolution of license plate configurations has varied from state to state. Many elementary and middle school teachers have found the origin of license plates an extremely interesting topic to explore with their students. It turns out that different states made different decisions about what to do when they ran out of combinations. Let's explore some of the configurations that have been used.

1. **M 728**

   a. An early license plate configuration consisted of a letter of the alphabet followed by 3 digits. With this system, how many possible license plates could a state make?

   b. A next step would be to simply add a digit — that is, use a letter followed by 4 digits. How many different license plates could be made this way?

   c. Let's say that your state uses the system in part (b) and is about to run out of license plates. What would you recommend next? Why?

2. **123 456**

   a. At some point, most states have used the following system: License plates consisting of a 6-digit number. How many possible license plates were possible?

   b. Let's say your state has been using the system in part (a) and is about to run out of license plates. What would you recommend next? Why?

3. **3 G 2346**

   a. Some states went for the pattern shown above: a digit, then a letter, followed by 4 more digits. How many possible license plates are there using this system?

   b. Many states discovered that 3 letters and 3 digits makes a sufficient number of combinations. How many possible license plates are there using this system?

4. Even with all these combinations, some states ran out of possible combinations. What would you recommend next? Why? How many different license plates could be made with your proposed system?

5.   Let's say a state outgrew the license plate consisting of 3 letters and 3 digits and was considering these two options: 1 letter, 2 digits, and 3 letters, or 6 letters. Which would you recommend? Why?

6.   Let's say a state decided to make a license plate that consisted of 6 letters. Theoretically, this would make $26 \times 26 \times 26 \times 26 \times 26 \times 26$ possible license plates. However, Mason has a problem. His calculator doesn't have enough spaces to show the exact answer; it only displays 8 digits. It shows 3.0891578 08. Explain how you could determine the actual answer with a *minimum* of pencil and paper computation.

7.   Let's say a state decided to have a license plate with the following format: 2 letters followed by three digits followed by 1 letter — for example, AB123C.

   a.   How many different license plates could be made with this system?

   b.   Maegen says that the answer here is the same as that for 3 letters followed by 3 digits. What do you think? Justify your answer.

EXPLORATION 7.15   **Native American Games**

Human beings have played games of chance for thousands, and perhaps tens of thousands of years. In 1975, Stewart Culin wrote a book *Games of the North American Indians.*[1] I was fascinated by the many different kinds of games of chance and the similarities and differences between games played by different tribes. This exploration uses some of the games in Culin's book and will help you to grapple with basic probability concepts, have some fun, and gain a sense of history.

   Each group will learn to play one of the games below and then explain the game to the rest of the class and report what they have learned about the game from playing and analyzing it. Each group will explore their game within the following parameters:

1.   Predictions. After playing for only a few throws, predict the answers to the following questions. Once you have made your own prediction, discuss your predictions in your group.

   a.   What is the probability of each way that results in scoring points?

   b.   What is the probability of getting no points on a throw?

   c.   How many different outcomes are there?

---

[1] Stewart Culin, *Games of the North American Indians* (New York: Dover Publications, 1975).

2. Experimental probability. Play the game for some time and determine answers to the first two questions in Step 1. That is, determine the experimental probabilities.

3. Theoretical probability. Determine the theoretical probabilities for all three questions in Step 1.

4. Presentations. In your presentation to the rest of the class, you must:

a. Demonstrate your game.

b. Give your answers to the three questions in Step 1, making sure that the listener can understand how you got your answers. You are free to make tables, charts, diagrams, and whatever other visual aids you consider helpful.

c. Share any other insights or questions about the game.

Part 1: A game from the Klamath tribe in California[2]

Four sticks are marked as shown at the right. The two sticks at the top are known as shnawedsh, (women), and the two bottom sticks are called xoxsha or hishuaksk, (men). The lines were made by pressing a hot, sharp-pointed tool against the wood. The other side of each stick is unmarked (plain).

The game consists of throwing the four sticks. The scoring is as follows:

- If all four marked sides face up, 2 points.
- If all four plain sides face up, 2 points.
- If both male sticks are up and the female sticks down, 1 point.
- If both female sticks are up and the male sticks down, 1 point.

You may make your own sticks or select other materials that will create an equivalent game.

Part 2: A game from the Nishinam tribe in California[3]

Two acorns have been split lengthwise in halves, and the outsides have been painted red or black.

The game consists of throwing the four acorn halves. The scoring is as follows:

- If all four painted sides face up, 4 points.
- If all four painted sides face down, 4 points.

[2] Culin, p. 136.
[3] Culin, pp. 154–155.

- If three painted sides face up, no points.
- If two painted sides face up, 1 point.
- If one painted side faces up, no points.

In this game, a player keeps throwing until a throw results in 0 points, and then it is the next player's turn.

You may make your own acorns or select other materials that will create an equivalent game.

Part 3: A game from the Songish tribe from British Columbia[4]

Four beaver teeth have been marked in the following manner on one side:

- Two teeth have been marked with a row of circles; they are called women.
- The other two teeth have been marked with cross lines; they are called men.
- One of the male teeth is tied in the middle with a small string and is called ihkakesen.

The game consists of throwing the four teeth. The scoring is as follows:

- If all four marked sides face up, 2 points.
- If all four marked sides face down, 2 points.
- If both male teeth are up and the female teeth are down, 1 point.
- If both female teeth are up and the male teeth are down, 1 point.
- If the ihkakesen is face up and the other teeth face down, 4 points.
- If the ihkakesen is face down and the other teeth face up, 4 points.

In this game, a player keeps throwing until a throw results in 0 points, and then it is the next player's turn.

You may make your own "teeth" or select other materials to create an equivalent game.

Part 4: A game from the Zuni tribe in New Mexico[5]

Four sticks have been painted red on one side; the other side is plain.

The game consists of throwing the four sticks. The scoring is as follows:

- If all four painted sides face up, 4 points.
- If three painted sides face up, 3 points.
- If two painted sides face up, 2 points.
- If one painted side faces up, 1 point.

In this game, a player keeps throwing until a throw results in 0 points, and then it is the next player's turn.

[4] Culin, p. 157.
[5] Culin, p. 223.

You may make your own sticks or select other materials that would create an equivalent game.

Part 5: Another game from the Zuni tribe in New Mexico[6]

Three sticks have been painted red on one side and black on the other side.

The game consists of throwing the three sticks. The scoring is as follows:

- If the three red sides face up, 10 points.
- If the three black sides face up, 5 points.
- If two red sides and one black side face up, 3 points.
- If one red side and two black sides face up, 2 points.

In this game, if three red sides face up, the thrower gets another turn.

You may make your own sticks or select other materials that would create an equivalent game.

Looking Back on Exploration 7.15

After the group presentations, each group will discuss the following questions.

1. In what ways were all of the games similar to one another — that is, what characteristics did they all have in common?

2. In what ways were some of the games different from some of the other games?

3. Describe your most important learnings from these games.

[6]Culin, p. 221.

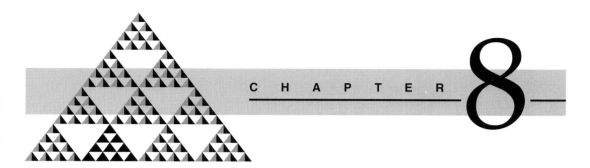

Geometry as Shape

Geometry is generally underrepresented in elementary school, partly because the geometry chapters occur at the end of most textbooks and partly because more emphasis is placed on developing students' skills in computation. Another reason is that many elementary teachers have negative feelings toward this area of mathematics because of bad experiences in high school geometry. Hopefully, you will be among the teachers who redress this imbalance.

At its root, geometry involves shape. In Chapters 9 and 10, we'll look at various applications of geometry and connections between geometry and other fields of mathematics. We will start with a couple of explorations that will orient you to a more geometrical way of thinking.

EXPLORATION 8.1   Geoboard Explorations

Geoboards are a popular manipulative in elementary schools and are very versatile. Many teachers also use them as a manipulative for learning about fractions. Smaller geoboards generally contain 25 pegs (5 rows of 5 in a row), and larger geoboards generally contain 100 pegs. There are also circular geoboards, generally with 24 pegs arranged in a circle. I know many teachers who have actually had their classes make a set of geoboards to save money, and the making of the geoboards—how much material to buy, where to put the nails, and so on—is a mathematics project in itself!

In Chapters 8 through 10, we will use geoboards to explore a number of mathematical concepts and to develop other problem-solving and reasoning tools.

PART 1: Communication

This first part of the exploration both serves as an introduction to geoboards and reinforces the need for clear communication when talking about shapes.

Instructions: In this exploration, you will work in groups of 3.

Persons A and B each have a geoboard or dot paper and sit back to back.

Person C is the observer.

Person A makes a figure on the geoboard. Next, using only words, person A gives directions so that person B can construct the same figure on his or her geoboard. The observer watches without comment, and will give feedback at the end. Person B's responsibility is to ask for clarification whenever person A's directions are not clear.

1. After you are finished, compare geoboards. The figures may or may not be identical. In either case, take some time to listen to person C's feedback and to discuss strategies that might increase the likelihood of success and discuss places where communication broke down.

2. Rotate roles: Person C now makes the figure and gives directions, person A makes the copy, and person B is the observer.

3. Repeat this process once more so that each person has a turn in each role.

4. Afterwards, write down your comments on the following:

   a. Describe strategies that increased the likelihood of success.

   b. Describe something you learned from this exploration.

PART 2: Challenges

If you have played with geoboards before or if you have visited classrooms where children were working with geoboards, you may have heard someone say, "I wonder if . . ."—for example, "I wonder if you can have a figure with exactly 3 right angles. I wonder how many different figures you can have that have only one peg inside."

The challenges below address a few of the hundreds of possible "I wonder" questions. Pursuing these challenges can help you develop problem-solving and reasoning skills and also help you to understand some of the properties of geometric figures.

Construct the following figures on your geoboard or explain why you think it is impossible.

1. a. A figure with just 1 right angle.

   b. A figure with 2 right angles.

   c. A figure with at least 1 right angle but no sides parallel to the edges of the geoboard.

d. A figure with 6 right angles.

2. A figure with exactly 2 congruent, adjacent sides.

3. Two figures with different shapes but the same area.

4. A triangle that touches 8 pegs and has 1 peg in the inside.

5. A square that touches 9 pegs.

6. **a.** A quadrilateral that touches 5 pegs and has 1 peg in the inside.

   b. A quadrilateral that touches 5 pegs and has 2 pegs in the inside.

   c. A quadrilateral that touches 8 pegs and has 1 peg in the inside.

   d. A quadrilateral that touches 8 pegs and has 2 pegs in the inside.

7. **a.** A figure that touches 5 pegs and has 1 peg in the inside.

   b. A figure that touches 5 pegs and has 2 pegs in the inside.

   c. A figure that touches 5 pegs and has 3 pegs in the inside.

   d. A figure that touches 5 pegs and has 4 pegs in the inside.

   e. A figure that touches 5 pegs and has 5 pegs in the inside.

   f. A figure that touches 5 pegs and has 6 pegs in the inside.

8. **a.** How big can a figure be that touches 5 pegs and has *x* pegs in the inside?

    b. Are there combinations of touching *x* pegs and having *y* pegs in the inside that you think are impossible?

9. What was your biggest learning from this exploration?

E X P L O R A T I O N   8.2   **Tangram Explorations**

Like geoboards, tangrams are very versatile manipulatives that we will use on several occasions in this and the next two chapters. Tangrams were invented in China at least two hundred years ago, but we are not sure by whom or what for. They quickly became a popular puzzle, because there are so many different things you can do with them! The English word *tangram* probably came from American sailors who referred to all things Chinese as Tang, from the Cantonese word for China.

You will use tangrams provided by your instructor or make your own set from the template at the back of the book.

PART 1: Observations, discoveries, and questions

The directions here are very simple: Play with them for a while. You may have questions for which you have some preliminary thoughts, and you may have some questions for which you don't have an initial response. As you explore the shapes, you will notice things: patterns and relationships among the various pieces. You will make interesting shapes. You may ask yourself various "what-if" questions.

Record your observations: patterns, discoveries, conjectures, and questions.

PART 2: Puzzles

As you may have found, you can make a number of interesting shapes with tangrams. Below are some famous puzzles that call for some careful thinking.

1. Can you make the following figures with all seven pieces?

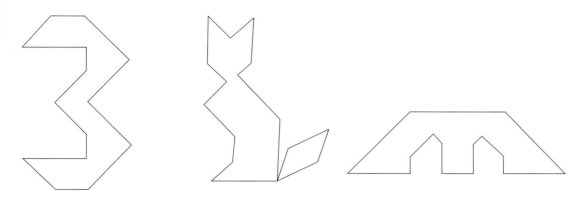

a. Describe any thinking tools that you became aware of while figuring out how to make the figures.

b. Describe any new observations: patterns, discoveries, conjectures, and questions.

2. This is a famous tangram paradox. Each of the figures below has been made with one tangram set. Yet it appears that the figure at the right has one more piece.

a. Solve the puzzle and show your solution. Describe any thinking tools that you became aware of while solving this puzzle.

b. Describe any new observations: patterns, discoveries, conjectures, and questions.

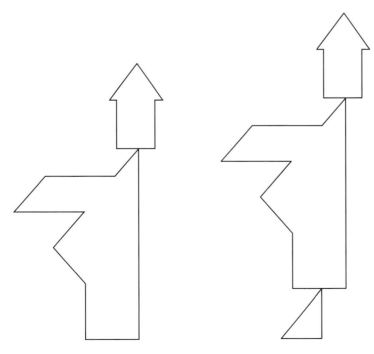

3.   Make your own puzzle. Name it. Give it to someone else to solve.

4.   Make a figure with the tangram pieces. Write directions for making that figure, as if you were talking on the phone to a friend. Exchange directions with a partner. Try to make the figure from your partner's description.

   a.   Discuss any problems that either of you encountered in understanding what the other had written.

   b.   Summarize what you learned from this step thus far.

   c.   Now make a new figure and write directions for making that figure, as if you were talking on the phone to a friend.

SECTION   8.1   **EXPLORING BASIC CONCEPTS OF GEOMETRY**

In order to work effectively with geometric ideas, we need to have a foundation of postulates, definitions, and theorems. As you may recall from high school geometry, the Greek contribution to geometry and mathematics is enormous. Though this textbook does not attempt to replicate the kind of formal geometric work you did in high school, I do believe it is helpful for elementary teachers to explore concepts and ideas that students will further examine in high school so that you have a better sense of the connection between the explorations you do in elementary school and the geometric knowledge the students will need to bring to middle school and high school.

EXPLORATION 8.3   **Defining Parallel and Perpendicular Lines**

The terms *parallel* and *perpendicular* occur both in algebra (equations of lines) and in geometry (properties of many geometric figures). This exploration requires you to think about these concepts and some of the algebra-geometry connections.

1.   On each of the geoboards below, make a line parallel to the given line. Develop, describe, and justify a rule or procedure for making sure that the two lines are parallel. The rule or procedure should be more precise than "It looks parallel."

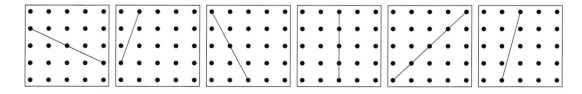

2. On each of the geoboards below, make a line perpendicular to the given line. Develop, describe, and justify a rule or procedure (beyond "it looks perpendicular") for making sure that the two lines are perpendicular.

EXPLORATION 8.4   **Seeing Patterns and Making Predictions**

This exploration contains several activities intended to develop your ability to think systematically, to see patterns, and to develop and test hypotheses that come from your observations, and to help you to see that algebra and geometry are not "disconnected" mathematical fields.

PART 1: Is it possible?

1. Fill in a table like the one below. Sketch your solutions. *Note:* There are multiple solutions for some cells in the table.

2. Extend the table to 8 intersecting points.

3. Extend the table to 9 intersecting lines.

4. Describe any generalizations you can make from this investigation.

Number of intersecting points in a plane

		0	1	2	3	4	5
Number of lines	2			Not possible	Not possible	Not possible	Not possible
	3					Not possible	Not possible
	4						Not possible
	5						
	6						

PART 2: How many regions?

When 2 lines in a plane intersect, four distinct regions are formed.

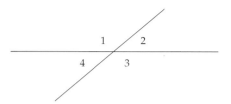

1.   If 3 lines intersect in a plane, what is the maximum number of regions that can be formed?

2.   If 4 lines intersect in a plane, what is the maximum number of regions that can be formed?

3.   If 5 lines intersect in a plane, what is the maximum number of regions that can be formed?

4.   If n lines intersect in a plane, what is the maximum number of regions that can be formed?

PART 3: How many lines?

If we take any 3 points that are not on the same line (noncollinear points), there are exactly 3 lines that can be constructed that will go through 2 of the 3 points. Thus, we can say that 3 noncollinear points determine 3 lines; that is, once you make the 3 points, those 3 lines are determined.

In a similar fashion, we find that any 4 noncollinear points will determine 6 lines. That is, regardless of where the 4 points are, as long as they are noncollinear, 6 lines are determined. See the figures on page 930.

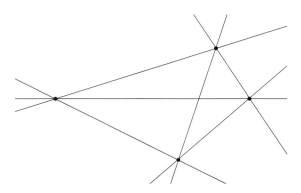

1.   How many lines are determined by 5 noncollinear points?

2.   How many lines are determined by 6 noncollinear points?

3.   Continue this exploration with 7 noncollinear points, 8 noncollinear points, and so on, until you see patterns that enable you to answer the following question: How many lines are determined by n noncollinear points? Your response to this last question needs to include the answer, a summary of how you determined the answer, and your justification of your answer (that is, explain to the reader why you believe your answer is correct).

S E C T I O N ◆ 8.2 ◆ **EXPLORING TWO-DIMENSIONAL FIGURES**

As you may already know, humans have been fascinated by various two-dimensional patterns for thousands of years. Many walls, ceilings, and floors have patterns. Patterns pervade many art forms. Understanding the properties of shapes and relationships between shapes enables the artist, the architect, and others to make interesting patterns and to design useful objects.

E X P L O R A T I O N 8.5 **Wankas, Smarfies, and More**

Mathematicians stress the importance of precise language when doing and discussing mathematics. Many students do not fully understand this need for precision and clarity and interpret the teachers' emphasis on precision as being "picky" or "technical." One of the goals of this exploration is to uncover the need for clarity in mathematics.

PART 1: New shapes

1.   In the group at the left below, there are four Wankas. None of the figures in the middle group are Wankas.

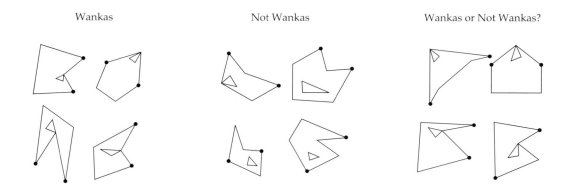

a. Describe the process that you will go through in order to determine which of the figures at the right are Wankas. Trying to articulate how you go about deciding what is and what isn't is an important part of mathematical thinking.

b. Determine which of the figures in the group at the right are Wankas. Justify your choices.

c. Discuss your results with other members of your group and then with the whole class.
      If you got any wrong, describe changes/refinements in how you go about the process that you can use in the next question.

d. Write a definition of Wankas.

e. Give this definition to someone who is not taking this class and ask that person to draw two or more Wankas from your definition. Describe the results.

2. In the group at the left below, there are four Smarfies. None of the figures in the middle group are Smarfies.

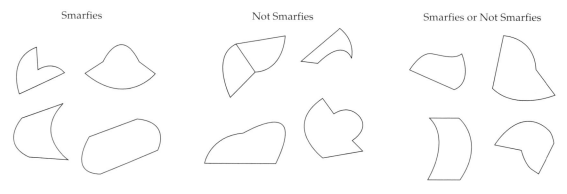

a. Describe the process that you will go through in order to determine which of the figures at the right are Smarfies. Trying to articulate how you go about deciding what is and what isn't is an important part of mathematical thinking.

b. Determine which of the figures in the group at the right are Smarfies. Justify your choices.

c. Discuss your results with other members of your group and then with the whole class.

If you got any wrong, describe changes/refinements in how you go about the process that you can use in the next question.

d. Write a definition of Smarfies.

e. Give this definition to someone who is not taking this class and ask that person to draw two or more Smarfies from your definition. Describe the results.

3. In the first group at the left below, there are four figures that are X's. None of the figures in the middle group are X's.

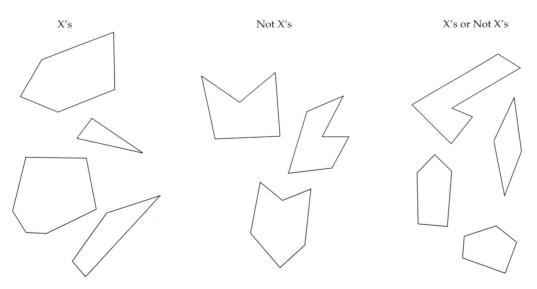

X's   Not X's   X's or Not X's

a. Determine which of the figures in the group at the right are X's. Justify your choices.

b. Discuss your results with other members of your group and then with the whole class.

   If you got any wrong, describe changes/refinements in how you go about the process that you can use in the next question.

c. Write a definition of X's.

d. Give this definition to someone who is not taking this class and ask that person to draw two or more X's from your definition. Describe the results.

4. In the first group at the left below, there are three figures that are Y's. None of the figures in the middle group are Y's.

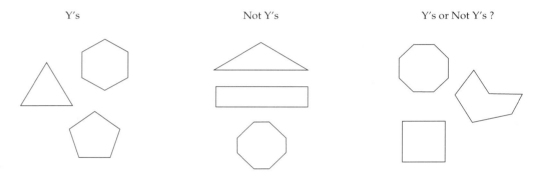

Y's   Not Y's   Y's or Not Y's ?

a. Determine which of the figures in the group at the right are Y's. Justify your choices.

b. Discuss your results with other members of your group and then with the whole class.

   If you got any wrong, describe changes/refinements in how you go about the process that you can use in the next question.

c. Write a definition of Y's.

d. Give this definition to someone who is not taking this class and ask that person to draw two or more Y's from your definition. Describe the results.

PART 2: 3RITs

In Chapter 9, we will explore the mathematics of quilting. One of the basic building blocks of many quilt patterns is the humble right isosceles triangle. In the figures on top of page 197, we have a "3RIT," that is, a figure made from 3 right isosceles triangles.

3 RIT   Not 3 RIT

1. Defining 3RITs.

   a. Discuss with your partner(s) your present thinking about what a 3RIT is. Draw more 3RITS and/or not 3RITS until you all agree on what a 3RIT is.

   b. On your own, write a precise definition of a 3RIT.

   c. Compare definitions with a partner with respect to accuracy and clarity.

   d. Modify your definition, if needed, so that it is accurate and clear.

2. Making 3RITs.

   a. Make as many different 3RITs as you can. Sketch (or tape or glue) them on a separate piece of paper.

   b. Compare results with members of your group.

3. Are the two 3RITs below different or not? Discuss this question until your group arrives at a consensus. Explain why you believe they are or are not different.

PART 3: 4RITs

1. Making 4RITs.

   a. Make as many different 4RITs as you can. Sketch (or tape or glue) them on a separate piece of paper.

b. Compare strategies and results with members of your group. Note any strategies mentioned in the discussion that you didn't use but that you liked. Also note any 4RITs that you didn't make.

2. Classification

a. Divide your set of 4RITs into two or more subsets so that each member of a subset has at least one characteristic in common. Name each subset (feel free to be creative), and describe the defining characteristic(s) of that subset. Sketch (or tape or glue) the members of each subset on a separate piece of paper.

b. Compare your results with members of another group.

Looking Back on Exploration 8.5

What did you learn during this exploration?

EXPLORATION 8.6   **Classifying and Naming Geometric Figures with Tangrams**

This exploration uses tangrams to explore the names and properties of different shapes.

The Two Small Triangles and the Medium Triangle

Using only the two small triangles and the medium-size triangle, make as many shapes as you can, with the following restriction: When two pieces meet, the whole side of one piece must fit against the whole side of another piece. Record your findings on a separate piece of paper by tracing the shapes.

1. Name each shape. If you know of a mathematical name, use it. If not, make up a name that relates to the shape.

2. Try to be systematic to ensure that you find all possible shapes. Describe how you were systematic. Try to explain your methods so that someone reading this description, as if through E-mail, could understand it.

3. Describe your other observations from this exploration: patterns, discoveries, conjectures, and/or questions.

The Two Small Triangles and the Square

With the same restrictions, make as many shapes as you can using only the two small triangles and the square. Record your findings on a separate piece of paper by tracing.

4.   Do you think you will be able to create as many, fewer, or more shapes than you were able to create in the first exercise? Explain your reasoning.

5.   Name each shape. If you know of a mathematical name, use it. If not, make up a name that relates to the shape.

6.   Describe your other observations from this exploration: patterns, discoveries, conjectures, and/or questions.

The Two Small Triangles and the Parallelogram

With the same restrictions, make as many shapes as you can using only the two small triangles and the parallelogram. Record your findings on a separate piece of paper by tracing.

7.   Do you think you will be able to create as many, fewer, or more than you were able to create in the first exercise? Explain your reasoning.

8.   Name each shape. If you know of a mathematical name, use it. If not, make up a name that relates to the shape.

9.   Describe your other observations from this exploration: patterns, discoveries, conjectures, and/or questions.

Connections

10.   You may have realized that in one part of the exploration above you made the "same" figure that you had made in another part. Go back to your drawings and record the figures that were made in all three parts, and in any combination of two parts.

11.   Discuss a way to communicate your findings, either with a diagram or with a chart. Make the diagram or chart.

12.   Compare your diagram or chart to that from another group.

13. If there were inaccuracies in your diagram or chart, note them and analyze both (a) the cause of the errors and (b) problem-solving tools whose use could have prevented the mistake.

14. Describe something "important" you learned from this exploration.

EXPLORATION 8.7   **Recognizing and Classifying Figures with Geoboards**

Geoboards can also be used to help students appreciate the need for names for various geometric figures and geometric ideas. If we were to look at the universe (remember Venn diagrams) of geometric shapes, there are countless possible subsets. In elementary, middle, and high school you learned the properties of a number of shapes, many of which have specific names. But a name implies certain characteristics. For example, there are all kinds of isosceles triangles, but regardless of their size and angles, all isosceles triangles have certain attributes in common. In this exploration, you explore different kinds of subsets from a small universe of geometric figures.

1. Cut out the Geoboard shapes at the end of this book.

2. Separate them into two or more subsets so that each subset is alike in some way.

3. Describe each subset so that someone who couldn't see your figures could get a good idea of what each subset looked like.

4. Name each subset. If you know of a mathematical name for a subset, use it. If you don't know of a mathematical name, make up a descriptive name that fits the subset.

5. Record the figures in each subset.

6. Repeat this process as many times as you can in the time given. That is, in what other ways can we separate these figures into two or more subsets so that every subset has one or more common characteristics?

Looking Back on Exploration 8.7

After the class discussion, note:

1. What did you learn from this exploration?

2. How do definitions help us to communicate when discussing geometry?

EXPLORATION 8.8   **Weird Triangles**[1]

Many teachers have done this exploration with middle school students. There is much food for thought for college students too in this exploration—from geometric ideas to problem-solving to reasoning.

Take a blank piece of paper. Fold it in half and then fold it in half again.

Draw a "weird" triangle—that is, any triangle—and then cut it out. You should now have four congruent triangles.

For each of the following questions, explain your reasoning.

1. Can you put these triangles together to make a large triangle?

2. Is there only one way, or are there different ways?

3. How could you prove that the new triangle is actually a triangle, as opposed to a figure that is almost a triangle?

4. Does the new large triangle have anything in common with the original triangle?

5. Repeat this activity with other weird triangles until you are satisfied with your responses to the four questions.

EXPLORATION 8.9   **Exploring Line Segments in Triangles**

In high school geometry, as you may recall, you spent more time studying triangles than any other figure, and theorems developed with triangles—about congruence, similarity, the sum of interior angles, and other topics—were extended to other polygons. Even though it is the simplest polygon (simply take three noncollinear points and connect them in turn), it is the most studied. The triangle is a powerful shape, a central figure in quilting and many other forms of art and construction. It is at the heart of the geodesic dome, which Buckminster Fuller invented. Fuller once remarked: "A triangle is the most economical and natural path a structure can take. Triangle is structure and structure is triangle. Period. It's what the whole Universe is based on."[2] Fuller sounds very much like a Pythagorean!

The following explorations are inspired by "what-if" games (a favorite game of young children, poets, scientists, inventors, and other curious people). They are designed to invite different kinds of ways in which people come to understand ideas—deductively, inductively, and intuitively.

[1] This exploration is adapted from a talk by Glenda Lappan entitled "The Connected Mathematics Project: Reaching All Kids Through Interesting Problems and New Instructional Strategies," given at the New Hampshire ATMNE meeting in Plymouth, New Hampshire, on April 1, 1994.
[2] Cited in Julian Weissglass, *Exploring Elementary Mathematics* (Dubuque, Iowa: Kendall Hunt Publishing, 1990), p. 161.

PART 1: The three medians of a triangle

1. What would happen if we drew the three *medians* of a triangle? How might you design your exploration of this question? Write down your thoughts about what would happen and how you might explore this question.

2. Compare notes with your partner(s).

3. Design a plan and then describe your plan so that your instructor can see your design and your work on the left side and your reflections and analyses on the right side.

4. Summarize your findings as conjectures.

5. Explore one or more of these questions. In each case, first state your initial response, then design your experiment, do the work, and report your findings.

   a. The point at which all three medians intersect is called the *centroid* of the triangle. The centroid divides each of the medians into two shorter line segments. What relationships can you find among the lengths of these line segments?

   b. Can other polygons have medians, or only triangles?

PART 2: The three angle bisectors of a triangle

1. Draw the three angle bisectors of a number of triangles. As before note your reflections and analyses on the right side.

2. Summarize your findings as conjectures.

3. Explore one or more of these questions. In each case, first state your initial response, then design your experiment, do the work, and report your findings.

   a. The point at which all three angle bisectors intersect is called the *incenter* of the triangle. If we find the centroid and incenter of a triangle, will they be the same point in some triangles? in all triangles? never?

b. Under what circumstances will the angle bisector also be a median?

c. Can we generalize our findings about incenters to other polygons?

PART 3: The three perpendicular bisectors of a triangle

1. Draw the three perpendicular bisectors of a number of triangles. As before, note your reflections and analyses on the right side.

2. Summarize your findings as conjectures.

3. Explore one or more of these questions. In each case, first state your initial response, then design your experiment, do the work, and report your findings.

a. The point at which all three perpendicular bisectors intersect is called the *circumcenter* of the triangle. If we find the centroid, incenter, and circumcenter of a scalene triangle, they will be different points; are they collinear or noncollinear?

b. Under what circumstances will the perpendicular bisector also be a median?

c. Can we generalize our findings about circumcenters to other polygons?

PART 4: A question of utility

Each of these three points—centroid, incenter, and circumcenter—has a useful role. One of the points (incenter) is the center of the circle that can be inscribed in the triangle (see the figure on the left below). Another (circumcenter) is the center of the circle that can be circumscribed about the triangle (see the figure on the right below). Yet another (centroid) is the center of gravity of the triangle. That is, if you made a triangle from heavy material (posterboard, wood, or metal), the triangle would balance at this point (see the figure in the middle below). Which will be which? Why?

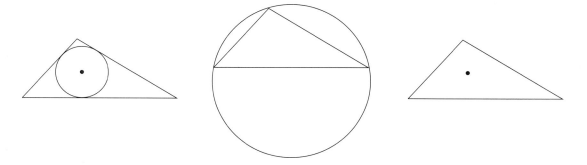

EXPLORATION 8.10 **Quadrilaterals**

Many people have negative feelings about geometry because they remember memorizing a lot of terms in elementary school and memorizing a lot of proofs in high school. This is unfortunate because the point of geometric knowledge is to have a better understanding of shapes in our everyday world, to better appreciate the aesthetics in natural and human-made shapes, and (in some occupations) to apply one's understanding of shapes. This exploration takes an inductive approach: From examining many different figures, what commonalities can you see?

PART 1: Properties

1. Get out six sheets of dot paper.

   a. On the first sheet, make several different squares.

   b. On the second sheet, make several different rectangles.

   c. On the third sheet, make several different parallelograms.

   d. On the fourth sheet, make several different rhombi.

   e. On the fifth sheet, make several different trapezoids.

   f. On the sixth sheet, make several different kites.

2. Examine each kind of quadrilateral and answer the following question: What characteristics and properties do all of the figures on this page have in common? For example, look at sides, angles, or diagonals, to name but a few ways to look.

3. Discuss your observations with others.

4. Summarize your findings in a table or diagram that will show the connections between common properties. For example, squares and rhombi both have four congruent sides, but squares and rectangles have four right angles.

PART 2: That's stretching it![3]

Many students report that this game really required them to think about the relationships among various quadrilaterals. You can play one person against another or one team against another.

Begin with the following parallelogram on your geoboard.

Roll two dice and refer to the table below to find out the characteristics of the new quadrilateral.

Convert the given quadrilateral to one with the new characteristics by moving as few corners as possible. On each successive roll, convert the quadrilateral you made on the previous roll.

CHARACTERISTICS OF NEW QUADRILATERAL

Number on second die

		1	2	3	4	5	6
	1	4 right angles					
	2	One pair of opposite sides congruent	No sides congruent or parallel				
Number on first die	3	No line of symmetry	Two pairs of parallel sides	One pair of opposite angles congruent			
	4	One pair of parallel sides	One diagonal a line of symmetry	One angle greater than 180°	One right angle		
	5	No sides parallel	Two pairs of opposite angles congruent	No sides equal	One pair of adjacent sides congruent	Two right angles	
	6	Two pairs of adjacent sides congruent	One obtuse angle	All four sides congruent	No angles congruent	Diagonal divides figure into two congruent figures	Two pairs of opposite sides equal

[3] This game has been adapted from George Bright and John Harvey, "Learning and Fun with Geometry Games," *Arithmetic Teacher,* April 1988, who based it on Thomas A. Romberg, John G. Harvey, James M. Moser, and Mary E. Montgomery, *Developing Mathematical Processes* (Chicago: Rand McNally, 1976).

Scoring: Before you begin the game, decide what will be a winning score. Then, score each roll as follows:

- 4 points if you need to move only 1 corner.
- 3 points if you need to move 2 corners.
- 2 points if you need to move 3 corners.
- 1 point if you need to move 4 corners.

Note: Even if the figure you make after rolling the dice has the same characteristics as the one on the board from the previous roll, you must still move at least one corner.

Variation: If your group feels that you can generate the new quadrilateral in fewer moves than the other and can demonstrate this, then you also score points according to the directions above.

SECTION 8.3 EXPLORING THREE-DIMENSIONAL FIGURES

How do you represent a three-dimensional object on paper? Why is this question important? Think about these two questions before reading on. . . . 📖

When we make complex objects, whether they be cars or houses or sculptures, they have to be designed first. Although scale models are often made, the actual construction is done from blueprints or drawings—that is, two-dimensional representations of the object. This ability to translate both ways between three-dimensional objects and two-dimensional representations of them is important in many parts of our life, yet there is evidence that this part of mathematics has been underemphasized in school in favor of more computational aspects of mathematics. In your work with children, it will be important that you provide them with opportunities to develop what we call spatial visualization abilities. More and more textbooks and other curriculum materials are emphasizing spatial visualization. It is very likely that you will do explorations like the ones below, at a simpler level, with your future students. The following explorations provide you an opportunity to work on these concepts and ideas and to do so in a way that should be both enjoyable and challenging.

EXPLORATION 8.11 3D to 2D Explorations

Here you will explore different possible ways to represent a three-dimensional object on paper. One of the beauties of this exploration is that there are many different ways to solve the problems, not just "the right way."

PART 1: How many cubes?

1. **a.** Look at the structure at the right. How many cubes were needed to make the structure? Work on this alone and briefly note your work.

   b. Compare strategies with other members of your group. Note any strategies that you like.

2. **a.** Look at the structure at the right. How many cubes were needed to make the structure? Work on this alone and briefly note your work.

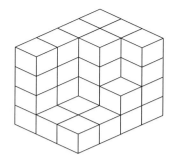

   b. Compare strategies with other members of your group. Note any strategies that you like.

3. **a.** Look at the structure at the right. How many cubes were needed to make the structure? Work on this alone and briefly note your work.

   b. Compare strategies with other members of your group. Note any strategies that you like.

   c. Write the minimum and maximum number of cubes that could be contained in the model at the right, if it is viewed from "ground level." Justify your answer.

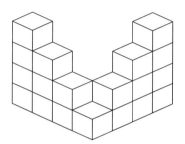

4. What did you learn from this exploration?

PART 2: Giving directions

A very major role that mathematics has played in the development of much technology is a process that is called mathematizing, that is, taking a situation or problem and using mathematics to better understand that situation or problem. Here you will grapple with how to give directions so that someone else can make a copy of a three-dimensional figure that you have constructed. If we make a block building from cubes (as in Part 1) and someone else wants to make that same building, that person can come to us and make a copy of that building right next to ours. If that is inconvenient, we could take a photograph, and the person could construct the building from the photograph. However, as you may have realized in Part 1, photographs can't show everything. Of course, we could photograph the building from all sides. That would solve the problem if we have a simple building (like the ones in Part 1), but it would not be useful for more complex buildings.

1. **a.** Make a building out of blocks and develop a way to communicate how to build that building to another group. Your communication may consist of words and/or diagrams.

b. Give your directions to another group and have them construct the building from your directions. Note any parts that they have difficulty with — that is, that they find confusing or ambiguous.

c. Switch roles, so that your group constructs a building from the other group's directions. Note any parts that you have difficulty with — that is, that you find confusing or ambiguous.

d. Repeat this process until you have developed a method that will enable another group to successfully build an exact copy of your block building.

2. Listen to methods developed by other groups. Note any ideas or comments that you heard that you liked.

3. Imagine you were an elementary teacher and students all over the country were making such buildings and comparing their work with other students. If you could choose among the different methods (via fax), which would you choose? Your response needs two parts: (1) an analysis of the pros and cons of each method, and (2) your choice and justification of your choice.

PART 3: Making drawings with isometric dot paper

We have explored different ways to communicate how to make block buildings. Now we will explore how to draw them. A special kind of dot paper called *isometric dot paper* (found in the back of the book) has been created to make such drawings easier. Make several copies of that page.

1. Draw the figure at the right on your dot paper. Many students find that it takes several rounds of guess–check–revise before their picture matches the one at the right. Once you succeed:

a. Describe strategies that you discovered while copying the shape.

b. Note other observations, insights, and questions (including what-if questions).

2. Practice with the figures below and/or make block buildings and then draw them. After these further explorations:

a. Describe new strategies that you discovered while making your drawing.

b. Note other observations, insights, and questions (including what-if questions).

3. **a.** Draw a building that contains between 10 and 15 cubes and is a "challenge" to draw — for example, a building with fewer cubes in a back row than in a front row.

b. Write the directions for making that building.

c. Explain any difficulties and how you overcame them.

PART 4: Interlocking cubes

1. What if you could make buildings with interlocking cubes, like the one below, for example?

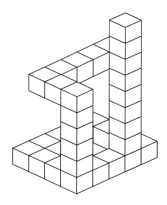

a. Make a complex building with interlocking cubes, and write directions for making the building, using any of the methods already devised or a new method (which could be a modification of previous methods). Have another group make the building using your directions.

b. Report the results. If it wasn't successful, explain the glitches and how you solved the glitches. Then repeat Step 1(a).

c. What did you learn from this?

2. What if the buildings were not restricted to cubes? Make a set of directions for one of the buildings below.

3. What did you learn from this exploration?

EXPLORATION 8.12   **Understanding Solids**

You found that each two-dimensional figure that has a name also has certain clearly stated attributes, and that there are various relationships among two-dimensional figures — for example, squares are closely related to both rectangles and rhombi. These observations are also true for three-dimensional objects.

PART 1: Describing solids

This first part is similar to the introductory geoboard exploration: How can you describe to someone else, using only words, what you are holding in your hand? Students will work in pairs.

1. Your instructor will show an object to the students who are facing the front. Using only words, these students will try to describe the object so that their partner can determine what it is. Afterwards, discuss the descriptions. If the students facing the back were able to decode the directions, great. If there were problems, analyze them, and then discuss how to revise the description to address the problems raised.

2. Switch roles and repeat the process with another object.

3. After the whole class discussion, record your observations, insights, and questions that you still have.

PART 2: Classifying solids

This second part focuses on understanding different relationships among three-dimensional figures.

Examine the objects (or pictures of objects) you have in front of you. As we have done in several other explorations, place the objects into two or more subsets so that the elements in each subset are alike in some way.

1. For each subset, describe the common attributes or properties, give a name to the subset (if you don't know of a mathematical name, make up a name), and list the members of the subset.

2. Repeat this process several times.

3. What did you learn from this exploration?

PART 3: Nets

Using posterboard, ruler, and scissors (or exacto knives), you will be asked to make nets for different figures. A net is a diagram showing what a hollow three-dimensional figure would look like if it were folded flat. For example, one net for the cube at the left is shown at the right.

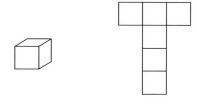

Two notes before you begin:

■ Before you cut anything, you have to have the complete net drawn on the paper.

■ The net cannot contain separate pieces. For example, the net above represents a valid way to make a cube. Cutting six squares of the same size and taping them together would be an invalid way.

1. Make a net for the figure at the right, a tetrahedron.

    a. Describe strategies that went beyond simple trial and error.

    b. Do you think there are other possible nets, or just this one?
        If you think there are others, sketch them.

2. Make a net for the figure at the right, a square pyramid.

    a. Describe strategies that went beyond simple trial and error.

b. Do you think there are other possible nets, or just this one?
  If you think there are others, sketch them.

3. Make a net for the figure at the right, a simple house shape.

  a. Describe strategies that went beyond simple trial and error.

  b. Do you think there are other possible nets, or just this one?
  If you think there are others, sketch them.

4. Make a net for the figure at the right, a cylinder.

  a. Describe strategies that went beyond simple trial and error.

  b. Do you think there are other possible nets, or just this one?
  If you think there are others, sketch them.

5. What did you learn from Part 3?

Extensions

1. Repeat Part 1 of this exploration with new objects.

2. Describe changes in your way of describing objects that you learned in this exploration.

E X P L O R A T I O N 8.13   **Cross Sections**

One important spatial visualization skill is being able to imagine what happens when physical objects are changed or moved — from being able to imagine how a new arrangement of furniture will work in a living room to being able to figure out if all of a set of objects will fit into a given space (such as a suitcase or the trunk of a car).

Here, we will explore the notion of cross sections. Consider the cube at the right. If we sliced it in half (as if a knife made a vertical slice), what would the newly exposed face (that is, the cross section) look like? If we sliced it at an angle, what would the new face look like now?

PART 1: Predictions

For each of the following, first predict what the sliced face will look like. Then check your prediction either by making a clay figure and slicing it or by some other means.

	Diagram	Predicted cross section	Actual cross section	Observations, insights, analyses
a				
b				
c				
d				
e				
f				

	Diagram	Predicted cross section	Actual cross section	Observations, insights, analyses
g				
h				
i				
j				
k				
l				

PART 2: Descriptions of intersections

In Part 1, you were given a picture representing a specific cross section of a solid object. What if you had no picture?

1. Describe an object and an intersecting plane, using only words.

2. Have another group describe what slice they would make, based on your description.

If they are able to accurately decode your directions, great. If there are problems, analyze them, and then revise the description to address the problems raised.

EXPLORATION 8.14   **Relationships Among Polyhedra**

Leonard Euler discovered a relationship among the number of vertices, the number of edges, and the number of faces of any *polyhedron*. Rather than present this relationship, I ask you to look at a variety of polyhedra below.

PART 1: Collecting data and making hypotheses

1. Count and record in a table like the one below the number of vertices, edges, and faces in each polyhedron.

2. What patterns do you see, and what observations or hypotheses do you have? Record them in the table. If you keep your mind open and use the problem-solving tools you have been developing, you will discover more than Euler's formula.

	Polyhedron	Number of vertices	Number of faces	Number of edges	Patterns, observations, or hypotheses
a					
b					
c					
d					
e					

	Polyhedron	Number of vertices	Number of faces	Number of edges	Patterns, observations, or hypotheses
f					
g					
h					

PART 2: Discoveries

1. Describe the relationship you found between the number of vertices, faces, and edges of any polyhedron.

2. Describe any significant actions that you took that facilitated this discovery.

3. Describe any other learnings from this exploration.

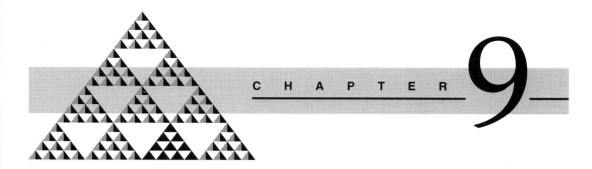

C H A P T E R 9

Geometry as Transforming Shapes

I n Chapter 8, we explored geometry from the perspective of shapes and properties. We discovered that the theme of composition and decomposition, which we first discovered with numbers, also extends to geometry. That is, by decomposing shapes, we can better understand their properties and their connections to other shapes. In this chapter, we are going to focus on transformations—that is, on what happens when we move shapes or modify shapes.

SECTION 9.1 **EXPLORING TRANSLATIONS, REFLECTIONS, AND ROTATIONS**

In this section, we will explore the effects of moving two-dimensional figures in various ways: by sliding the shape (called a *translation* of the shape), by flipping the shape over (called a *reflection* of the shape), and by turning the shape (called a *rotation* of the shape).

EXPLORATION 9.1 **Reflections (Flips)**

In this exploration, we will focus on understanding what happens to a figure when it is reflected across a line and when it is reflected across more than one line. In doing so, you will not only learn more about reflections, but also develop the ability to make and test predictions.

PART 1: Similarities

In the left part of the figure below, we see the effect of reflecting triangle *CAN* across a line. Triangle *C'A'N'* is called the reflection image of triangle *CAN*. In the right part of the figure, we see the effect of reflecting rectangle *PONY* across a line.

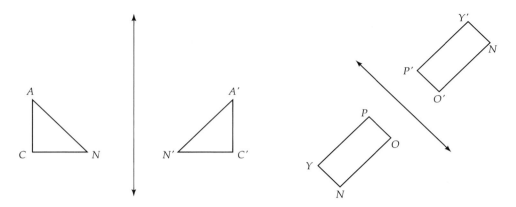

There are some similarities and some differences between the two reflections. In the first case, we reflected a triangle; in the second case, a rectangle. In the first case, the *line of reflection* was a vertical line; in the second case, the line of reflection was a diagonal line. In the first case, a single vertex was closest to the line of reflection; in the second case, one whole side of the figure was closest to the line of reflection. In this exploration, you will be asked to discover the common characteristics of all reflections. For example, we found that all rectangles have certain characteristics, such as four sides and four 90-degree angles.

1.   With a partner, draw a figure and a line and find the reflection image. Repeat this process a number of times.

2.   Describe the set of characteristics that are true in all cases in which a figure is reflected across a line.

PART 2: Two reflections

Now that you have examined the operation of reflecting a figure across a single line, let us examine the operation of reflecting a figure across two lines in turn.

1.   We will first explore the effect of reflecting a figure across two lines that are parallel.

   a.   Predict the reflection image of trapezoid *STAR* if we first reflect it across line *l* and then reflect that image across line *m*. Sketch where you think the image will be. Briefly explain your prediction.

   b.   Now, do the actual reflections. If your prediction was way off, describe what you learned from this activity so that future predictions will be more accurate.

c. Predict the reflection image of trapezoid *STAR* if we first reflect it across line *m* and then reflect that image across line *l*. Sketch where you think the image will be. Briefly explain your prediction.

d. Do the actual reflections. If your prediction was way off, describe what you learned from this activity so that future predictions will be more accurate.

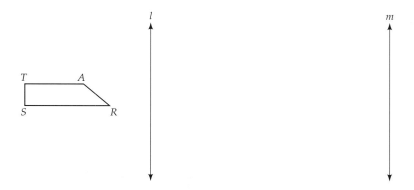

2. Describe any hypotheses you have about the effect of reflecting a figure across two parallel lines.

3. You found that when we reflected trapezoid *STAR* across line *l* and then across line *m*, we did not get the same result as when we reflected it first across line *m* and then across line *l*. If we let *X* represent any figure, we can symbolize this observation as $Xlm \neq Xml$. From one perspective, reflection across a line is an operation on a figure. This is analogous to the operation of addition. In the case of addition, we are operating on numbers. When working with numbers, we found that the operation of addition is commutative and that the operation of subtraction is not commutative.

a. What about the operation of reflection? Are there any cases in which this operation will be commutative? What do you think?

When mathematicians wish to investigate a phenomenon, they often work systematically, exploring different cases. Let us explore another case: What if the figure is between the two parallel lines? Where will the reflection image lie? In this case, will $Xlm = Xml$?

b. Predict the reflection image of triangle *RAP* in the figure below if we first reflect it across line *l* and then reflect that image across line *m*. Sketch where you think the image will be. Briefly explain your prediction.

c. Do the actual reflections. If your prediction was way off, describe what you learned from this activity so that future predictions will be more accurate.

d. Predict the reflection image of triangle *RAP* if we first reflect it across line *m* and then reflect that image across line *l*. Sketch where you think the image will be. Briefly explain your prediction.

e. Do the actual reflections. If your prediction was way off, describe what you learned from this activity so that future predictions will be more accurate.

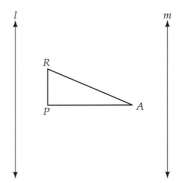

4. Do you think there is any scenario in which *Xlm* and *Xml* will be equal when *X* is reflected across two parallel lines? Explain your reasoning.

5. Let us now examine reflections across perpendicular lines.

a. Predict the reflection image of trapezoid *CONE* if we first reflect it across line *l* and then reflect that image across line *m*. Sketch where you think the image will be. Briefly explain your prediction.

b. Do the actual reflections. If your prediction was way off, describe what you learned from this activity so that future predictions will be more accurate.

c. Predict the reflection image of trapezoid *CONE* if we first reflect it across line *m* and then reflect that image across line *l*. Sketch where you think the image will be. Briefly explain your prediction.

d. Do the actual reflections. If your prediction was way off, describe what you learned from this activity so that future predictions will be more accurate.

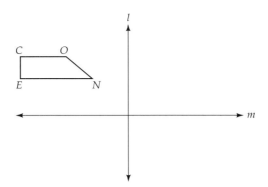

6. We found that reflection of this figure across these two perpendicular lines was commutative. Do you think this will always be the case? For example, what if the base of the figure was not parallel to one of the lines of reflection?

    a. Describe your initial hypothesis and briefly explain your reasoning.

    b. Do a number of reflections on your own. Show this work. In each case, briefly explain why you picked the figure that you picked.

    c. Describe your present hypothesis and briefly explain your reasoning.

7. Is there any other transformation that could achieve the same result as reflecting a figure across two parallel lines? State your thinking and support your statement.

EXPLORATION 9.2 **Tessellations**

Section 9.1 includes some basic facts about tessellations—basic figures that do and don't tessellate, and why. These explorations are designed to enable you to delve more deeply into tessellations—to connect geometric ideas you have learned in Chapter 8 and Section 9.1 and to bring to life other aspects of mathematical thinking that it is important that you develop: making and testing predictions.

PART 1: Which figures do and don't tessellate?

On page 222 are six pairs of figures. In each case, determine which of the figures in a pair will tessellate: both, just one, or neither. If both of the figures tessellate, make and justify a generalization: All figures that "look like" these two and have the following characteristics (describe the characteristics), will tessellate.

　　If just one of the figures in a pair tessellates, explain why the one does tessellate and why the other doesn't. That is, what characteristics or properties does the one figure have that the other doesn't have?

　　If neither of the figures tessellates, describe whether you believe that modifications of the figure could be made so that figures that "look like" these two might tessellate.

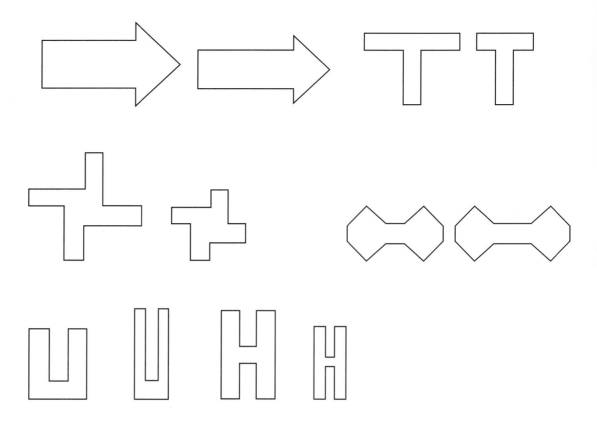

PART 2: What kinds of pentagons will tessellate?

As is explained in the text, the regular pentagon does not tessellate. However, some pentagons *do* tessellate. Under what conditions will a pentagon tessellate? It is expected that you will make and test several different kinds of pentagons. In each case, briefly describe the thinking behind the pentagons that you make. That is, why did you make a pentagon that had these particular characteristics?

   Tips: Fold a piece of paper in half, then in half again, and then in half again. Now if you make a figure and then cut out the figure (with heavy scissors), you will have 8 copies of the figure. Alternatively, you can make a figure using a software program and then cut and paste many copies of the figure.

   There are three parts to your evaluation:

1.   Your conclusion in the following form: If a pentagon has the following characteristics (listed), then it will tessellate.

2.   Your justification of your conclusion.

3.   Your work—that is, the pentagons that you made up and tested to see whether they tessellated or not.

PART 3: Semiregular tessellations

Now let us expand our discussion to combinations of figures that tessellate. A semiregular tessellation occurs when two or more regular polygons tessellate and every vertex point is congruent to every other vertex point.

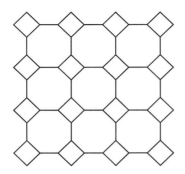

1. **a.** Using your understanding of congruent, try to define *congruent vertex point*.

    b. Compare your definition with your partner(s). Modify your definition, if needed, as a result of the discussion.

2. Explore combinations of simple geometric figures to determine other semiregular tessellations. Make copies of the Regular Polygons sheet at the end of the book.

    a. Sketch your "successes" and "failures" and record your reflections after each success or failure.

    b. How many semiregular tessellations do you think there are—5, 10, 20, 50, 100, thousands, an infinite number? Explain your reasoning.

3. In your explorations, you may have found some demiregular tessellations—when two or more regular polygons tessellate, but in which not every vertex point is congruent to every other vertex point. Show any demiregular tessellations that you have discovered. Explain why they are not semiregular tessellations.

PART 4: Copying tessellations

Many of the tessellations we have examined up to now are fairly simple, and we can easily copy them. However, many tessellations are very complex, especially when we add color. Look at the tessellation on page 224, which was found on the floor of a Roman house of the first century A.D.[1]

[1] Lorraine Mottershead, *Metamorphosis: A Source Book of Mathematical Discovery* (Palo Alto, Calif.: Dale Seymour Publications, 1979), p. 96.

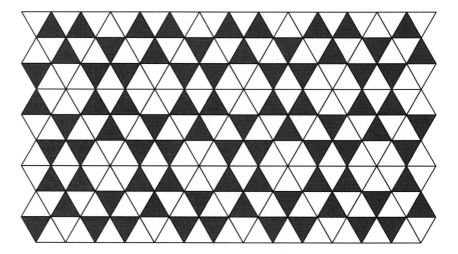

1. Describe the patterns you see in this tessellation.

2. Compare your observations with those of your partners.

3. Your next task will be to reconstruct the pattern on another piece of paper. You will be asked to do so in a manner other than mechanically copying the figure triangle by triangle. Discuss strategies for doing so with your partners. Then reconstruct the pattern and describe how you did so in such a way that if you faxed these directions to a friend, that person could reconstruct the floor pattern as you did.

4. What did you learn during this step?

5. After hearing how other groups reconstructed the floor, summarize what you learned from hearing these other groups.

EXPLORATION 9.3   Escher-like Tessellations

Using the language of translations, reflection, and rotations, we are now in a position to understand how M. C. Escher made his tessellations. Escher began with a polygon that would tessellate and then transformed that polygon. We can use the analogy of chess to understand how he did this: There are legal moves and illegal moves.

1. *Translations.* One legal move is to modify one side and then translate (which is the same as a vertical or horizontal slide) that modification to the opposite side:

Step 1   Step 2   Step 3

   a. Begin with a square and experiment with translations. Show your work and reasoning so that your instructor can follow your thinking. Make notes of your observations as they happen: patterns you see, conjectures that you decide to pursue, questions that you have.

   b. Summarize what you learned (observations, patterns, hypotheses) about translations and tessellations.

2. *Rotations.* Another legal move is to rotate part of a shape. The center of rotation — that is, the "hinge" about which the part rotates — can be a vertex or a midpoint of one of the sides. For example,

Begin with an equilateral triangle

Transform one side

Rotate that side counterclockwise through the bottom left vertex

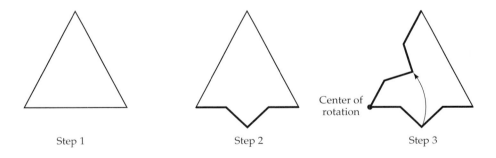

Step 1   Step 2   Step 3

   a. Begin with a square and experiment with rotations. Show your work so that your instructor can follow your thinking. Make notes of your observations as they happen: patterns you see, conjectures that you decide to pursue, questions that you have.

b. Summarize what you learned about rotations and tessellations.

3. *Combinations of translations, rotations, and reflections.* We can combine translations, rotations, and reflections to make tessellations. For example, we can begin with a rectangle and, using a compass and straightedge, construct a semicircle whose diameter is half the length of the side of the rectangle.

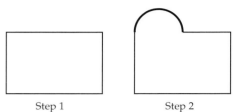

Step 1   Step 2

We can then rotate the semicircle 180 degrees, with the center of rotation being the midpoint of the top side of the rectangle.

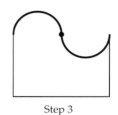

Step 3

Next, we translate this shape to the bottom side of the rectangle.
This shape will tessellate, but it's not very interesting.

Step 4

However, we can also transform the shorter side of the rectangle. This time, we replace half of the right side of the rectangle with a quarter circle whose radius is equal to the length of the line segment we are replacing.

Step 5

Then we *reflect* (another legal move) that quarter circle across a line parallel to the base of the rectangle and going through the middle of the rectangle.

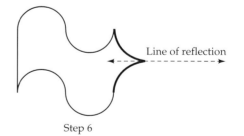

Line of reflection

Step 6

Finally, we translate this side of the rectangle to the other side. The original rectangle is shown with dotted lines.

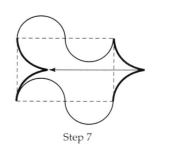

Step 7

a. Begin with a square and experiment with combinations of translations, reflections, and rotations. Show your work so that your instructor can follow your thinking.

b. Summarize what you learned about combinations of translations, rotations, and reflections and tessellations.

4. Each of the figures below tessellates, and each began as a basic geometric figure. Can you determine the starting polygon and how the shape was made?

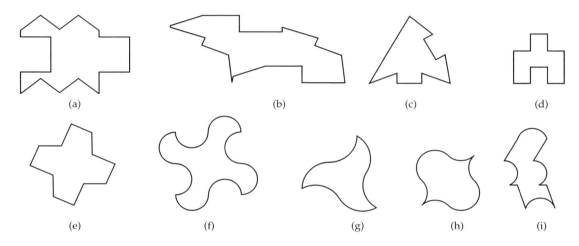

(a)　　　　　　　(b)　　　　　　　(c)　　　　　　　(d)

(e)　　　　　　　(f)　　　　　　　(g)　　　(h)　　　(i)

5. Make your own tessellations!

EXPLORATION 9.4　**Pentominoes**

Polyominoes were invented by Solomon Golumb, an American mathematician, in 1953, and they have been used since then by elementary, middle, secondary, and college teachers to explore different mathematical ideas and to develop problem-solving skills. A polyomino is any geometric figure that is composed entirely of squares. You are most familiar with one subset of polyominoes made with two squares, which we call dominos. There are several parts to our exploration with polyominoes, some of which involve slides, flips, and turns, and some of which involve other mathematical ideas and skills.

PART 1: Defining pentominoes

1. A pentomino is a figure made up of five connected squares. Write down your definition of pentomino.

Pentomino　　　　Not a pentomino　　　Not a pentomino

2.   Compare your definition with other group members' definitions. Revise your definition, if you choose. If you do revise your definition, explain what you revised and why.

PART 2: How many pentominoes?

1.   How many "different" pentominoes can be made? Show your solutions. Describe any tools other than random trial and error that you used in your search.

2.   Once you think you have found all of the pentominoes, describe why you think you have them all.

3.   As a class, come up with a name for each different pentomino. This is necessary to make communication easier.

PART 3: Slides, flips, and turns with pentominoes

1.   There are four pairs of figures below. In each case, the top figure was transformed into the bottom figure by a slide, flip, and/or turn. Describe what was done to the top figure to create the bottom figure.

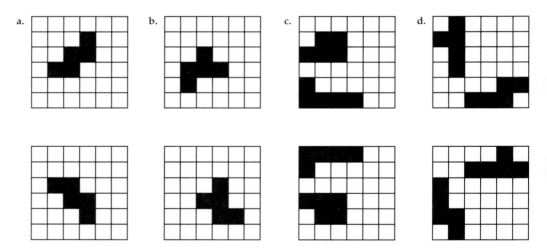

2.   Describe what was done to the top figure to create the bottom figure.

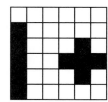

3. Make your own figures on the top row. Then transform the figure by making any combination of slides, flips, and/or turns. Describe what you did. Give your problems to a friend and see if your friend can guess your transformations.

a.   b.   c.   d.

         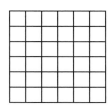

PART 4: Classifying pentominoes

1. We can classify pentominoes in many different ways. For example, some will make a box (with no lid) when folded.

   a. Predict which ones will make a box (with no lid) when folded.

   b. Meet with your partner. Compare your predictions and reasoning.

   c. Determine which pentominoes do make boxes. If there were any that did make boxes that you didn't predict or any that didn't make boxes that you thought would, reflect on your reasoning. That is, now that you know the answers, can you add to your spatial reasoning tools, describe new tools, or refine old ones?

   d. Identify any common characteristics of those pentominoes that do make a box as opposed to those that do not make a box. Can you develop a function for predicting which pentominoes will make boxes? If so, the input set will be the characteristics common to all box-making pentominoes only.

2. Classify the pentominoes by their perimeter. Identify any common characteristics of those with the same perimeter.

3. Describe other possible ways to classify pentominoes.

4. Describe other patterns and observations from your explorations with pentominoes.

PART 5: A pentomino game

Make a chessboard (8 × 8 square). Each square in the pentomino is the same size as each of the 64 squares on the board.

Players take turns placing one pentomino on the board.

The winner is the last person who can place a pentomino on the chessboard so that it does not extend beyond it and does not lie on top of a previously played pentomino.

1. Play the game several times. Describe any strategies you discovered.

2. Play a cooperative version: Find the set of moves that results in the smallest number of pentominoes being placed on the board.

a. Show your solution.

b. Describe any strategies you discovered.

PART 6: Pentomino challenges

1. Using your whole set of 12 pentominoes, arrange the pentominoes so that the space enclosed by the pentominoes is as large as possible.

2. For each of the following rectangles, can you make the rectangle using a subset of your set of pentominoes? Is there more than one different solution?

a. 3 × 10

b. 4 × 5

c. 5 × 5

3. Select the pentominoes that are shaped like the following capital letters: T, U, Z, W, and P.

For each one of these five shapes, a similar figure can be made by using four pentominoes (of any shape). The solution for T is shown.

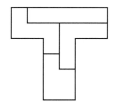

a. Take a few minutes to think about making a U, Z, W, or P. What ideas do you have beyond a random guess–check–revise?

b. Share your thoughts with your partners. Together, make a figure similar to one of these pentominoes.

c. At the most basic van Hiele level, the larger figures are similar in appearance to the smaller figures. However, if we analyze the smaller and larger figures, we can find mathematical relationships between the two figures. Take some time in your group to grapple with this concept of similarity, which we will explore in depth in Section 9.3. Draft a definition of similarity that you can then test on these figures.

PART 7: Creativity with pentominoes

Make the most creative picture you can with your whole set of pentominoes. Name the picture.

PART 8: Pentominoes and tessellations

1. Which of the pentominoes will tile the plane? Justify your response.

2. Make a tessellation pattern with your pentominoes. You need to use at least two different pentominoes.

EXPLORATION 9.5   **Understanding Congruence**

When I have done number theory explorations like Exploration 4.3 (Factors) with children and when I have done Pentominoes with children, we always spend some time discussing when two figures are the same. For example, some children will vehemently argue that the two figures below are different, while others will argue that they are the same.

In one sense, both students are right. Whether you see them as "the same" depends on the context. For example, on several occasions, when I was moving into an apartment or house and wanted to see how I might arrange my living room, I made a scale model of the living room and scale models of the furniture. A figure like the one

above might represent an easy chair. In this case, the figures are "different" because their orientation makes a big difference.

 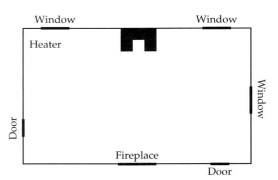

What is the same about them is that they have the same shape and size. Mathematically, we say that the two figures are congruent. The concept of congruence is important, and the following activities have you explore congruence relationships with two different manipulatives.

PART 1: Congruence with geoboards

On page 233 are three pairs of figures.

1. Which, if any, pairs are congruent?

2. How can you tell without cutting them out and placing one figure on top of the other?

3. Discuss this question and then develop a test that someone else could use to determine whether two figures are congruent or not.

Pair 1

Pair 2

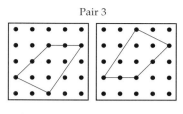
Pair 3

PART 2 : Congruence with tangrams

1. We can make a trapezoid with the tangram's parallelogram and the two little triangles, and we can make a trapezoid with the tangram's medium triangle and the two little triangles. Are the two trapezoids congruent? How could you prove that they are or are not?

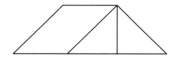

2. Is each of these pairs of tangram figures congruent? Explain your reasoning.

   a.

   b.

      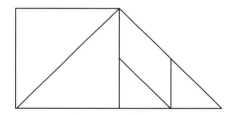

SECTION ◆ 9.2 ◆ **EXPLORING SYMMETRY**

Symmetry is one of those mathematical concepts that we find virtually everywhere! We find it in the natural world—at the microscopic level and at the galactic level. We find it in plants and animals. We find it in everyday life and in the arts. In some cases, it has aesthetic value; in other cases, very practical value. We find it in every human culture ever known!

EXPLORATION 9.6   **Quilts**

There are so many places to explore symmetry and so little time in this course! I have focused on quilts because quilts are rich in symmetry, they can be explored with young children, and they lend themselves to an interdisciplinary approach to learning literature, history, and mathematics.

Quilting has a fascinating and ancient history. While we cannot definitely mark the date of the first quilt, we know that in the transition from hunter-gatherers to farmers many thousands of years ago, the development of agriculture inspired experiments with new ways to keep warm at night other than using animal hides, leaves, straw, and other such material. The oldest remnants of what we might call quilts—that is, spreads with patterns on them—are well over two thousand years old. Various cultures developed different patterns and techniques. We know that the Crusaders brought the idea of quilting back to Europe from the Middle East. However, an event in the fourteenth century caused quilting to come into its own: Europe suffered through what is referred to as the Great Freeze, year after year of very severe winters. This added need for more warmth at night spurred many advances in quilting, including the quilting frame. After the Great Freeze, a much greater percentage of women made quilts, and it was one of the few activities that was engaged in by poor and rich alike!

The origin of what has been called patchwork quilting is also interesting. It developed out of pioneer life in the early years of this country's history. As pioneers moved westward, more and more people lived far from stores, and the notion of "having to make do with what you've got" became a part of life. The amount of garbage generated by pioneers was a small fraction of what families throw away today. After making clothes, women would have various pieces of leftover fabric. Rather than throw them away, they would cut the pieces into small triangles, squares, and other geometric figures. The triangle was a common choice because one could get the most from scraps by cutting out triangles. (Why is this?) In many areas, wintertime was the quilting party season because there was little farm work to be done. Women would gather to trade scraps, trade ideas, work together, and socialize.

Many of the quilt designs in this exploration have a rich history. Almost any public library will have many books on quilting, and with a bit of research you can probably find a quilting group in your own town!

PART 1: Beginning simple

The *block* is the basic unit of a quilt. Blocks are usually squares (and we often call them *squares*), but some quilts' blocks are hexagons or other shapes.

1. **a.** Examine the quilt block below. This basic unit has been constructed from 8 right isosceles triangles using 2 colors. Describe the construction of this block in terms of translations, rotations, and reflections. You are describing the block's *pattern*, which is sometimes called the *quilt s* pattern. (Quilting terminology is not always precise!)

   b. Examine the shape below at the right, which was created by putting together four copies of the quilt block. (A quilt is made by sewing many blocks together.) Describe the new designs and shapes that you see. Explain why these designs came about.

A block

Four blocks

2. Take 8 right isosceles triangles and put them together in some way to form a block. Your block does not need to be a square. Sketch your pattern; that is, sketch what your block looks like.

3. Work in groups of 4.

    a. Select one person's block and have each member copy that block.

    b. Predict the shapes that will emerge when you put these 4 congruent blocks together.

    c. Put the four blocks together. Describe the new patterns and shapes that you see. Explain why these patterns came about.

    d. Repeat the process.

    e. Sketch one figure that emerged from combining the 4 congruent blocks.

    f. Describe where the new patterns came from.

PART 2: Exploring actual quilt patterns

"There are two kinds of people in this world: those who divide everything into two groups and those who don't."[2] We hope that the various times you have been given a set of objects and asked to separate them into subsets, you have found value in the exercise. We will do this with quilts, for each quilt has many attributes.

1. Take a minute or so for each member of your group to silently examine each quilt pattern on the next page. Then, one by one, describe what you see. That is, member 1 describes what is seen in the first pattern. If member 2 saw something different, that is noted. After each member has noted any additional observations, examine the second pattern. This time member 2 goes first, and so on.

2. Now make a copy of the next page and cut out the quilt blocks. Separate these blocks into two or more groups in such a way that each group has one or more common attributes. Describe the common attribute(s) and name each group. Repeat this as many times as you can in the time provided.

---

[2] Kenneth Boulding, cited in Michael Serra, *Discovering Geometry — An Inductive Approach* (Berkeley: Key Curriculum Press, 1993), p. 88.

Baby blocks   Broken windows   Cross roads   Does and darts

Drunkard's path

Flower basket

Hole in the barn door

Kansas sunrise

Le Moyne Star   May basket   Saw Tooth Star   Star

Storm at Sea

Snail's Trail

Old Tippecanoe   Tulip Basket

Windmill   Yankee Puzzle

3. What did you learn from classifying the blocks and discussing the classifications?

All quilt patterns have a story. The stories behind some of these quilt blocks are given below. These stories are adapted from *Eight Hands Round: A Patchwork Alphabet*, by Ann Paul, one of many interesting books on quilting.[3]

Old Tippecanoe:

This was the nickname of William Henry Harrison, the ninth U.S. President. When he was a general, he defeated a group of Native Americans at the Tippecanoe River in Indiana. I am not sure whether this pattern was inspired by a representation of the battle or some other characteristic of Harrison.

Storm at Sea:

This pattern represents a lighthouse, with the center square representing the light. Before modern technology, lighthouses were built at the most dangerous points along the coast.

Windmill:

Windmills used the wind as a source of power so that people could mill their grain. That is, the windmill (and water wheel) would generate enough power to turn a millstone, which would crush the grain and turn it into flour.

Yankee Puzzle:

Ann Paul notes that many years ago, people in New England often played with a puzzle that had seven small pieces—five triangles, one square, and one rhombus—which they would arrange into different designs. I find the parallels between this and the Chinese tangrams interesting.

PART 3: Making quilt patterns

Each member of the group will select one or two quilt patterns from Part 2 and draw the pattern at home. Each drawing of a quilt pattern should measure 6 inches by 6 inches. You can use ruler, pencil, compass, protractor, and/or computer software.

1. Bring the following to the next class:
   a. Your drawing

   b. Your description of how you did it, including measurements

   c. A description of any difficulties and how you overcame them

[3] Ann Paul, *Eight Hands Round: A Patchwork Alphabet*

d. Any new insights, observations, or discoveries from making the pattern

2. Reexamine the whole set of quilt patterns shown in Part 2. Classify them now according to how they are made—that is, according to commonalities in their mathematical structure.

3. What did you learn from this part of the exploration?

PART 4: Different symmetries

Consider the set of quilt patterns in Part 2, plus the ones below.

1. Determine which patterns have rotational symmetry. Classify them according to the kind of rotational symmetry that they have.

2. Determine which patterns have reflectional symmetry. Classify them according to the kind of reflectional symmetry that they have.

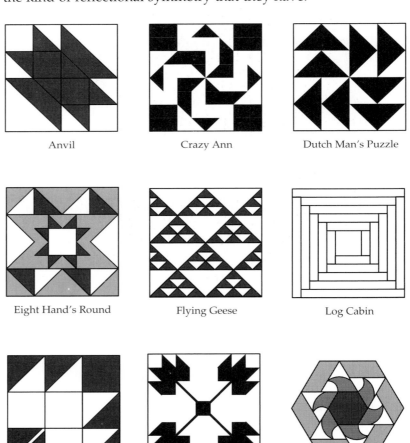

Anvil	Crazy Ann	Dutch Man's Puzzle
Eight Hand's Round	Flying Geese	Log Cabin
Maple	Peony	Starry Nights

Susannah   Rabbit Paw   Underground Railroad

Anvil:

In earlier times, most towns had a blacksmith who made things from iron by placing the metal in a fire until it became soft enough to have its shape changed by pounding it with a hammer against an anvil. The blacksmith made axes, farm tools, horseshoes, and other things that had iron components. The anvil had both a straight part and a curved part. When the blacksmith wanted to make the iron straight, he placed the iron on the flat part of the anvil. When he wanted to make the iron curve, he placed it on the curved part of the anvil.

Eight Hands Round:

At various times, people in an area would gather together: for a barn raising, a quilting bee, or some other occasion. In the evening, there would usually be some music and some dancing—square dancing and/or contra dancing. Someone would "call" the dances, that is, give instructions throughout the dance. One of the calls was "eight hands round," which meant for the four couples in a square to join hands in a circle.

Log Cabin:

When the American settlers moved to the frontier, they had to make their own homes from the wood in the forest. You have surely heard the stories about Abraham Lincoln's being born in a log cabin. This pattern was inspired by someone's creative representation of the pattern of the logs in a log cabin.

Underground Railroad:

The Underground Railroad was a network of people who helped slaves escape from slavery. A slave trying to get to a state where slavery was illegal often had to travel hundreds of miles. Those people who helped the slaves fed and hid them, usually at night, and then gave them directions to the next safe place.

3. Using different colors of construction paper, cut out a number of squares and triangles.

    a. Make a pattern (a block) that has rotational symmetry but not reflection symmetry. Briefly convince the reader that the figure does have rotational but not reflection symmetry.

b. Make a pattern that has reflection symmetry but not rotational symmetry. Briefly convince the reader that the figure does have reflection but not rotational symmetry.

c. Make a pattern that has both reflection symmetry and rotational symmetry. Briefly convince the reader that the figure does have rotational and reflection symmetry.

PART 5: Colors and patterns

Make an original quilt block from the construction paper pieces of Part 4, Step 3, or replicate one of the patterns given in Part 4. Experiment with the effect of different colors and different ways of combining the quilt blocks (that is, constructing a quilt using that block). Describe why you find that combination of blocks appealing. This may include symmetries, shapes, proportions, colors, and other attributes. Display your work.

PART 6: Quilts and tessellations

1. *The Bow Tie.* Many of the designs *within* quilt blocks will tessellate, especially if we focus on the pattern inside the squares.

    a. Consider the Bow Tie quilt square at the left. What if we take away some of the corners to expose the Bow Tie by itself as shown on the right? Will this part of the pattern tessellate? What do you think? Make your prediction and explain your reasoning.

    b. Compare notes with your partner. If you change your mind, describe what caused you to change.

    c. Check it out. Modify the bow tie to make a figure that will tessellate. Explain your thinking.

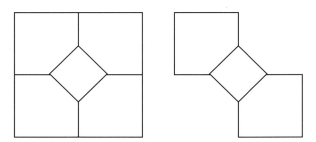

2.   *Squares and rectangles.*

    a.   Below is a quilt design called Brick Wall. (Large and small squares are sewn together to make a quilt.) Why does this design itself tessellate?

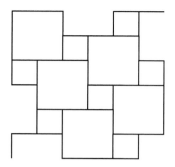

    b.   Can you make a variation of this design that also tessellates?

    c.   Can you make a variation with rectangles?

3.   *Bachelor s Puzzle.* This is an Amish quilt design called Bachelor's Puzzle.

    a.   Make a copy of the design. Describe how you made it.

    b.   Does it tessellate? Justify your answer.

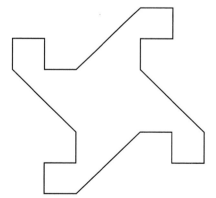

4.   *Making your own quilt tessellations.*

    a.   Find three different patterns within quilt blocks that we have examined in this section that tessellate or will tessellate upon modification.

   b. Make an original design that tessellates. Describe how you made it and what
   you like about the design.

EXPLORATION 9.7   **Lattices and Geometric Structure**

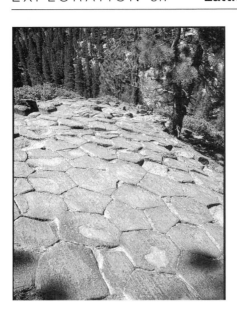

Crystals have fascinated humans for many
thousands of years. Throughout the ages,
and even today, many people have attributed
certain powers to crystals. A question that
puzzled people for thousands of years was,
"Why do only a few kinds of rocks have
these orderly shapes?" For example, the basalt
rocks shown in the photo have formed in a
hexagonal pattern. The origin of the word
crystal gives a clue to early hypotheses — the
word comes from the Greek word for ice. By
the seventeenth century, even before modern
atomic theory, scientists were hypothesizing
that the shapes of crystals were due to an
orderly, patterned internal structure. Some
suggested that crystals are made of stacks of tiny
spheres or bricks that represented the basic
particles of the structure, whatever those might
be.[4] Sphere packings and bricks are still
important models for crystal structure today.

   This notion of an orderly array connects to the mathematical concept of lattices. A
one-dimensional lattice is essentially a set of dots that are evenly spaced along a line.
One-dimensional lattices are not terribly interesting, but two-dimensional lattices both
are interesting mathematically and have applications beyond mathematics. A two-
dimensional lattice may be thought of as a repetition of row after row of one-
dimensional lattices. The dots on each row can be directly under each other, or the
rows can be shifted so that the dots in every other row have been moved (translated)
horizontally. This creates many possibilities.

   This exploration comes from a question that relates to ideas in physics. Imagine
that each dot occupies all the space (on the paper) that is closer to it than to any
other dot. Imagine drawing a fence to denote the space that is closer to a given

   dot than to any other dot; that is, the fence would be the set of points in "no
man's land." Each one of these regions bordered by a fence is called a Dirichlet
domain.

PART 1

1. *Square lattice.*

   a. Determine the Dirichlet domains for the lattice on page 243.

---

[4] Marjorie Senechal, *On the Shoulders of Giants,* p. 155.

b. Describe how you solved the problem.

c. Predict the shape of the fence for the lattice shown in Step 2—in that case, the dots are still below each other, but the vertical distance between two adjacent dots is greater than the horizontal distance between two adjacent dots. Explain the reasoning behind your prediction.

2. *Rectangular lattice.*

a. Determine the Dirichlet domains for the lattice below.

b. Describe how you solved the problem.

   c. Predict the shape of the fence for the lattice shown in Step 3—in that case, every other row of dots has been translated horizontally. Explain the reasoning behind your prediction.

3. *Staggered lattice.* Determine the Dirichlet domains for the lattice below. Describe how you solved the problem.

PART 2

1. What other possible lattices might produce different kinds of regions? Write down your thoughts, and then discuss your ideas with your partner(s) and determine how you could create those lattices and find new Dirichlet domains.

2. Describe your findings.

3. *Another staggered lattice.* Determine the Dirichlet domains for the lattice on page 245. Describe how you solved the problem.

(dot grid)

Looking Back on Exploration 9.7

1. What generalizations can you make about Dirichlet domains?

2. Will all Dirichlet domains have symmetry? If so, will they have the same kind of symmetry? If not, why not?

SECTION   9.3   **EXPLORING SIMILARITY**

EXPLORATION 9.8   **Similarity with Pattern Blocks**

In Chapter 5, we used Pattern Blocks to explore fraction concepts. These blocks also let us see geometry "in action."

PART 1: Triangles

1. Take the small green triangle. Using the Pattern Blocks, make a bigger triangle that is similar in shape to this triangle. Explain why you believe this triangle is similar to the original triangle.

2. Make another triangle that is similar to the original triangle. Explain why you believe this triangle is similar to the original triangle.

3.   Record other observations: patterns, hypotheses, conjectures, and questions. For example, are there patterns in the lengths of the sides, in how large the figures are, in how you actually make larger figures?

PART 2: Squares

1.   Take the small orange square. Using the Pattern Blocks, make a bigger square that is similar in shape to this square. Explain why you believe this square is similar to the original square.

2.   Make another square that is similar to the original square. Explain why you believe this square is similar to the original square.

3.   Record other observations: patterns, hypotheses, conjectures, and questions. For example, are there patterns in the lengths of the sides, in how large the figures are, in how you actually make larger figures?

PART 3: Parallelograms

As it turns out, all equilateral triangles are similar to one another, and all squares are similar to one another. This is not true for all parallelograms!

1.   Take the small blue parallelogram. Using the Pattern Blocks, make a bigger parallelogram that is similar in shape to this parallelogram. Explain why you believe this parallelogram is similar to the original parallelogram.

2.   Make another parallelogram that is similar to the original parallelogram. Explain why you believe this parallelogram is similar to the original parallelogram.

3.   a.   Write your first draft of a definition of *similar* with respect to parallelograms. Your definition should be more precise than "same shape, possibly different size."

     b.   Compare your definition with that of your partner(s). After the discussion, modify your definition, if needed.

4.   Record other observations: patterns, hypotheses, conjectures, and questions. For example, are there patterns in the lengths of the sides, in how large the figures are, in how you actually make larger figures, and so on?

PART 4: Trapezoids

1.   Take the small red trapezoid. Using the Pattern Blocks, make a bigger trapezoid that is similar in shape to this trapezoid. Explain why you believe this trapezoid is similar to the original trapezoid.

2.   Make another trapezoid that is similar to the original trapezoid. Explain why you believe this trapezoid is similar to the original trapezoid.

3.   Record other observations: patterns, hypotheses, conjectures, and questions. For example, are there patterns in the lengths of the sides, in how large the figures are, in how you actually make larger figures, and so on?

4.   Which of the following trapezoids is similar to the small red trapezoid? Justify your reasoning.

5.   **a.**   Write your first draft of a definition of *similar* with respect to any geometric figure. Be precise, as noted in Part 3.

b.   Compare your definition with that of your partner(s). After the discussion, modify your definition, if needed.

Looking Back on Exploration 9.8

There is a pattern concerning the area of consecutive similar Pattern Blocks that is true for all of the blocks: The ratio of the area of the next bigger similar figure to the original is 4:1. That is, if we count the area of the green triangle as 1 unit, the next bigger equilateral triangle has an area of 4 units. The blue parallelogram has an area of 2 units, and the next bigger blue parallelogram has an area of 8 units. Thus, the ratio of their areas is 4:1. This is also true for the orange square, the red trapezoid, and the yellow hexagon.

1. Do you think this is true only in these cases, or will it be true for composite figures too? For example, will the area of the next bigger figure similar to this one be 4 times as great as this one?

EXPLORATION 9.9   **Similarity with Tangrams**

PART 1: Rectangles

1. **a.** With your group, make as many different rectangles as you can, using the pieces from one set. Make a copy of each rectangle by tracing it.

    b. Compare your results with those of another group (or the whole class). Add any new drawings of rectangles to your group's collection.

2. **a.** Separate the set of rectangles into subsets so that all the rectangles in a subset are similar to each other.

    b. Describe how you determined which rectangles are similar. Then write a definition or a rule for *similar* rectangles.

    c. Share your definition with other groups.

PART 2: Trapezoids

1. Make as many different trapezoids as you can, using the pieces from one set. Make a copy of each trapezoid by tracing it. Compare your results with those of another group (or the whole class). Add any new drawings of trapezoids to your group's collection.

2. **a.** Separate the trapezoids into subsets so that all the trapezoids in a subset are similar to each other.

    b. Use your rule/definition from Part 1 to determine which trapezoids are similar. If it still works, move on. If it doesn't, explain why, and then modify your rule/definition.

c. Share your definition with other groups.

d. If your definition/rule has changed, note the change and why you like this version better than your original version.

Looking Back on Exploration 9.9

1. Can you extend your definition of similarity to any geometric figure? Make a tangram figure that is not a triangle or a quadrilateral. Now make a similar figure on another sheet of paper. Explain how you did it and justify your solution.

2. Irma says that all of the triangles that you can make with tangrams will be similar to one another. What do you think of Irma's conjecture? Explain your reasoning.

EXPLORATION 9.10   Similarity with Geoboards

1. On dot paper, make new figures (one per page) that are "similar" to each of the figures below. How do you know that your new figures are similar to the given ones?

   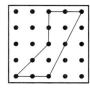

2. Discuss this question and then develop a test that someone else could use to determine whether two figures are similar or not.

EXPLORATION 9.11   Similar Figures

PART 1: Similar triangles

In high school geometry, we discovered that we did not have to show that all six pairs of corresponding angles and sides were congruent in order to know that two triangles were congruent. We learned about SSS, SAS, ASA, AAS, and HL. What might we need to show in order to know that two triangles are similar? Once again, the goal is to find shortcuts. At this point, in order to know that the two triangles are similar, we need to measure the lengths of all six sides and all six angles, and then we have to determine three ratios. If all the ratios are equal and all three pairs of angles are equal, then we know the two triangles are similar.

$$\frac{AB}{PQ} = \frac{AC}{PR} = \frac{BC}{QR} \quad \text{and} \quad m\angle A = m\angle P, m\angle B = m\angle Q, m\angle C = m\angle R$$

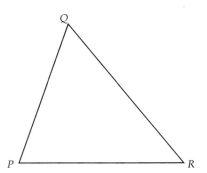

The question is: Do we have to know all the ratios to determine whether two triangles are similar? What combinations of sides and angles will be sufficient?

1. Write your initial hypothesis and reasoning about *one* combination that is sufficient to prove that two triangles are similar.

2. Discuss your ideas with your partner(s). Take one hypothesis; try to convince yourself that it is true, and try to make triangles that are not similar but that satisfy your hypothesis.

3. Present your hypotheses to another group. Note any comments or suggestions made by the other group.

4. Work through Part 1 repeatedly (as time permits) in order to convince yourself of as many similarity combinations as you can.

PART 2: Similar quadrilaterals

The figure below shows a pair of similar rectangles and a pair of similar trapezoids. At this stage of our explorations, to confirm that they are indeed similar, we would have to measure all eight sides and all eight angles and verify that the lengths of corresponding pairs of sides had the same ratio and that corresponding angles were congruent. The question is: Do we have to know all eight pieces of information? What combinations of sides and angles will be sufficient?

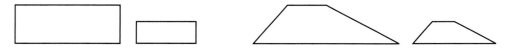

1. Rectangles

    a. Write your initial hypotheses and reasoning for rectangles.

    b. Discuss your ideas with your partner(s). Take one of your hypotheses; try to convince yourself that it is true, and try to make rectangles that are not similar but that satisfy your hypothesis.

    c. Present your hypotheses to another group. Note any comments or suggestions made by the other group.

2. Trapezoids. Repeat Step 1 for trapezoids.

Looking Back on Exploration 9.11

Come up with a conjecture that will work for all quadrilaterals. That is, if these conditions are met, then the two quadrilaterals will be similar. Justify your conjecture.

EXPLORATION 9.12   Reptiles

Solomon Golumb (see Exploration 9.4) invented reptiles, figures that both tessellate and also replicate themselves (as explained in Part 1 below). What began as an interesting thought turned into an idea with powerful real-life applications.

PART 1: A trapezoid reptile

Consider the trapezoid below.

    This trapezoid tessellates. Now we will see how it "replicates itself." We can divide this trapezoid into four smaller congruent trapezoids, each of which is similar to the original—sort of like having children!

1. Why is "reptile" an appropriate name for such figures?

2.   Prove that the four little trapezoids are similar to the larger trapezoid.

3.   **a.**   Make another trapezoid that is a reptile.

      b.   Describe the attributes that a trapezoid must have in order to be a reptile.

4.   How many different ways can you find in which this trapezoid will tile the plane?

5.   Some tessellation patterns have a lattice structure and some do not. A lattice is an arrangement of dots that follow a regular geometric pattern. The different kinds of dot paper in the Appendices are examples of lattices. A geoboard represents a simple lattice. When considering whether a tessellating polygon has a lattice structure, we need to focus on the dots that are the vertices of the polygon. Do some or all of the trapezoid reptile tessellations have no lattice structure? "Tilings without lattices are of great interest today among mathematicians and solid-state scientists because they share many strange properties with some recently discovered crystalline materials called quasicrystals."[5]

PART 2: A hexagon reptile

The hexagon below is another reptile.

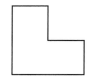

1.   Determine how to divide this hexagon into several little congruent hexagons, all of which are similar to the original.

2.   How many different ways can you find in which this hexagon will tile the plane?

3.   Do some or all of the hexagon reptile tessellations have no lattice structure?

[5] Marjorie Senechal, "Shape," in *On The Shoulders of Giants,* p. 159.

Looking Back on Exploration 9.12

1.   Based on these two examples, hypothesize some of the characteristics that a polygon must have in order to be a reptile.

2.   Discover another polygon that is a reptile.

EXPLORATION 9.13   **Quilts and Proportions**

PART 1: The Spool

The quilt block on the left below is called the Spool. Quilters say the Spool is a *9-patch pattern* because it can be made from 9 *patches*, or 9 smaller squares, as shown at the right below.

  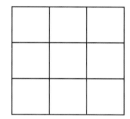

Having examined close to 100 quilt books and many quilts in person, I know that, not surprisingly, there have been many variations of standard quilt patterns over the years. In other words, quilters have played the "what-if" game. Let us play one round here.

1.   What if we made a version of the Spool pattern but used a 5-patch design or a 7-patch design? See the grids representing various patch layouts below. (You'll notice the inconsistency in quilting terminology: The 9 in "9-patch" refers to the number of little squares, but the 5 in "5-patch" refers to the dimensions of the square; that is, it is a 5 by 5 square.) How would the appearance of a 5-patch Spool differ from the 9-patch Spool shown above?

   a.   Describe your thoughts.

   b.   Compare your descriptions with those of your partner(s).

2.   Now make a 5-patch version of the Spool that has the same size block.

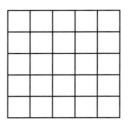

     a.   Compare the lengths of the sides of the squares in the middle and the surrounding trapezoids.

     b.   Compare the areas of the squares in the middle and the surrounding trapezoids.

3.   Now make a 7-patch Spool. Before calculating, predict the ratio of sides and areas for the 9-patch, 5-patch, and 7-patch versions of the Spool. Explain your reasoning.

Looking Back
What did you learn from this exploration?

PART 2: Attic Windows
Here are two variations of another famous quilting pattern called Attic Windows.

1.   How can we use the idea of patches to construct the Attic Windows pattern? Make some different Attic Windows patterns and "play" with them. Describe your observations and discoveries.

2. Write directions for making an Attic Windows pattern as if you were sending it by E-mail, where you could use only words.

PART 3: Drunkard's Path

Another famous quilting pattern is called the Drunkard's Path.

Before we examine the Drunkard's Path block and variations, let us analyze the pattern itself. Like many other patterns, this one has many variations. The figure on the left represents one block. The figure on the right shows four blocks put together to make the desired pattern. There are many different ways to put together the basic block, and some of these different ways have names of their own: Fool's Puzzle, Falling Timbers, Wonder of the World, and Lone Ring.

1. Describe what you see. Assume that a friend missed class today but has the pattern at the left. Write down what you will say on the telephone to help your friend make the design at the right.

2. Experiment with Drunkard's Path blocks whose individual patterns have different proportions. Which do you like best? Why?

3. Play with different patterns that can be made with multiple copies of the basic Drunkard's Path. Submit your favorite one, and explain why you like it. Give it a name.

PART 4: Squares inside squares

1. Make a larger copy of the quilt block at the right. You can choose the dimensions of the block.

2. Determine the ratios of the lengths of the sides of the 6 squares in the block and the ratios of the areas of the 6 squares.

3. If you were to use this color scheme (that is, dark and light), how much of each color would you need if each block was 9 inches by 9 inches and the quilt consisted of 72 blocks—that is, if it were 81 inches by 72 inches?

PART 5: Triangles inside triangles

1. Make the quilt block at the right, and describe how you made it. You can choose the dimensions of the block.

2. Determine the ratios of the sides of the different-sized triangles that are similar.

3. Determine the ratios of the areas of the different triangles that are similar.

4. Shade in the quilt according to various schemes from Pascal's triangle.

PART 6: Stars and Squares

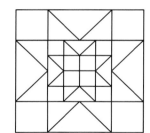

1. Describe what you see. Compare descriptions with those of your partner(s).

2. Make the quilt block, and describe how you made it. You can choose the dimensions of the block.

3. Observe the figure as long as you wish, then draw the figure from memory. Then describe your thinking process.

4. Is the star in the center of the figure mathematically similar to the large star? Why or why not?

5. Let us compare the areas of the two stars. At the most basic level, we can say that the big star is much bigger than the little star in the middle. How much bigger is the bigger star?

    a. Without doing any measuring or computation on paper or with a calculator, describe your thoughts. Explain your thinking.

b. Compute and compare the areas of the two figures.

c. If we made a littler star inside the little star, what would its area be?

Geometry as Measurement

Many, if not most, uses of basic mathematics involve measurement. Formulas are important because they enable us to answer the "how much?" questions more efficiently. However, for many prolems, there is no formula (for example, what is the area of your state?). In other cases, you need to apply measurement ideas to solve nonroutine problems (for example, to find the height of a tree). In this chapter, you will explore important measurement ideas and also come to understand why various formulas work.

SECTION ◆ 10.1 ◆ **EXPLORING SYSTEMS OF MEASUREMENT**

As you have already realized, much of our use of numbers involves measurement: how much, how many, how far, and so on. In this section, we will examine some of the issues surrounding linear measurement—that is, situations in which we want to ask questions or gain information about distances, heights, and thicknesses. We will also work with measuring weight and begin thinking about area and volume.

EXPLORATION 10.1 **How Long?**

As you did in Alphabitia, for a moment imagine that you are back in time before there were feet or meters or standardized tools to measure them. Your tribe wants to make a community building, and they want the length and width of this building to be exactly the length and width of your classroom.

1. Using only the tools your instructor provides and your own reasoning, with your partners, determine the length and width of the room.

2. Present your method and your answer to the class.

3. What did you learn about measurement from this exploration?

EXPLORATION 10.2 **How Tall?**

In many cases, we obtain a linear measurement without measuring the object directly. For example, we might read that the distance from New York to Los Angeles is 2,825 miles and that the Sears Tower in Chicago is 1,454 feet tall. These numbers were not determined using tape measures! What do you do when you cannot measure something directly?

1. Your instructor will select an object (tree or building) for which you will determine the height.

    a. Brainstorm reasons why someone might actually want to know the height of this object.

    b. Brainstorm ideas for determining the height.

2. Select and pursue one method with your group. Describe and justify each step in your plan.

3. **a.** Justify the precision in your answer—that is, the choice of unit and the degree of accuracy: for example, to the nearest 10 feet (meters), 1 foot (meter), one decimal place, and so on.

    b. Describe and explain your degree of confidence in your result.

    c. Describe any difficulties you had and how you overcame them.

4. Present your group's findings to the class.

5. Which group's method do you think will produce the answer closest to the actual height? Justify your response.

6. What did you learn about measurement from this exploration?

EXPLORATION 10.3   **How Thick?**

Most of our linear measurements use units like inches, feet, or miles, or the corresponding metric units. However, people in many occupations need measurements of amounts that are very small. For example, how thick is your skin? What is the wavelength of red light? How long is an amoeba?

Let us explore how we might answer one such question: How thick is one sheet of paper?

1. With your partner(s), brainstorm ideas for answering this question.

2. Select and pursue one method with your group. Describe and justify each step in your plan.

3. **a.** Justify the precision in your answer — that is, the choice of unit and the degree of accuracy, for example.

  b. Describe and explain your degree of confidence in your result.

  c. Describe any difficulties you had and how you overcame them.

4. Present your group's findings to the class.

5. Which group's method do you think will produce the answer closest to the actual thickness? Justify your response.

6. What did you learn about measurement from this exploration?

EXPLORATION 10.4   **How Much Is a Million?**

Researchers have told us that many people's behavior with numbers is very different when the size of the numbers becomes greater than they can actually imagine. For example, we can concretely imagine how much space would be taken up by 100 people listening to a musician play, but it is hard to imagine how much space would be taken up by a concert audience of 1 million people.

Many elementary school teachers have told me that when they ask, for example, "How large does a container need to be to hold one million paperclips?", children invariably underestimate. They give responses such as "a jewelry box" or "a cereal box."

PART 1: 1 million dollars

Betty has just won 1 million dollars in 1-dollar bills!

1. How much do you think 1 million dollar bills will weigh?

    a. Write down your estimate and any reasoning behind the estimate.

    b. With your partners, devise a plan for answering this question and then carry out that plan.

    c. Present your results to the class.

    d. What did you learn about measuring and about problem-solving from this problem?

2. What if we made a road with these dollar bills, in which each row consisted of ten 1-dollar bills? How long would the road be?

    a. Write down your estimate and any reasoning behind the estimate.

    b. With your partners, devise a plan for answering this question and then carry out that plan.

    c. Present your results to the class.

    d. What did you learn about measuring and about problem-solving from this problem?

3. What if we were to stack these dollar bills in a room, putting a rubber band around sets of 100 dollar bills? What would be the dimensions of a room that would hold one million dollar bills?

    a. Write down your estimate and any reasoning behind the estimate.

    b. With your partners, devise a plan for answering this question and then carry out that plan.

    c. Present your results to the class.

    d. What did you learn about measuring and about problem-solving from this problem?

PART 2: 1 million pennies

1. How much do you think 1 million pennies would weigh?

    a. Write down your estimate and any reasoning behind the estimate.

    b. With your partners, devise a plan for answering this question and then carry out that plan.

    c. Present your results to the class.

    d. What did you learn about measuring and about problem-solving from this problem?

2. In *The Wizard of Oz*, Dorothy walked down the yellow brick road. What if we made a road that was 2 feet wide with 1 million pennies? How long would the road be?

    a. Write down your estimate and any reasoning behind the estimate.

    b. With your partners, devise a plan for answering this question and then carry out that plan.

   c.   Present your results to the class.

   d.   What did you learn about measuring and about problem-solving from this problem?

3.   What if we were to stack these 1 million pennies in a room, after first putting groups of 50 pennies into rolls? What would be the dimensions of a room that would hold one million pennies?

   a.   Write down your estimate and any reasoning behind the estimate.

   b.   With your partners, devise a plan for answering this question and then carry out that plan.

   c.   Present your results to the class.

   d.   What did you learn about measuring and about problem-solving from this problem?

Looking Back on Exploration 10.4

1.   State and then describe something important that you learned from this exploration.

2.   State and explain any questions you have about π at this point.

SECTION   10.2   **EXPLORING PERIMETER AND AREA**

We encounter the need to know perimeters and areas in our everyday and work lives. In determining perimeters and areas, we need many ideas and formulas that have been developed over the centuries.

EXPLORATION 10.5   **Tangrams and Measurement**

PART 1: Angles

1.   Determine the sizes of the angles in each of the seven tangram pieces found at the end of this book *without the use of a protractor* (that is, by reasoning alone). Explain how you did this.

2.   Check your answers with a protractor. If you made any mistakes, determine where you went wrong.

PART 2: Area

1.   Determine the relative size of each tangram piece.

    a.   First, write down what you understand the task to mean. That is, in your own words, describe what you understand "determine the relative size of each piece" to mean.

    b.   Record the order in which you determined the relative sizes. That is, which did you determine first: the biggest triangle, the smallest triangle, the square, or some other piece?

    c.   Now meet with a partner or with another group. Each person or group reports its findings. The other person or group listens actively. Note anything you learned from this discussion.

2.   In the standard tangram package, the hypotenuse of the small triangle is 2 inches long.

    a.   Determine the length of each side of each of the seven pieces without measuring, by examining relationships between pieces and using the Pythagorean theorem. (For a right triangle with legs a and b and hypotenuse c, $a^2 + b^2 = c^2$.) Explain your work.

    b.   Now determine the actual area (in square inches) of each figure. Explain your work.

3.   **a.**   Why do you think the standard tangrams are the size that they are?

b. What if the sides of the small squares were 1 inch? What would be the dimensions of the other pieces?

4. Using the dimensions of the actual tangram pieces, determine the area of the *arrow*. The shaded region is made from the tangram pieces.

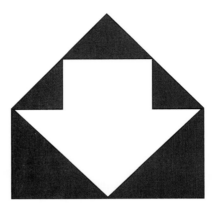

EXPLORATION 10.6   **Exploring the Meaning of Area**

What Does Area Mean?

1. Let us begin by exploring what area means—not how we determine it, but what it means. Imagine that someone from another planet came to visit, and that when you made a comment like, "The area of this figure is greater than the area of that figure," the person asked you what *area* means. How would you respond? Write your response (your first draft) and then compare responses with your partner(s).

What Does the Number Mean?

2. Consider a rectangle whose dimensions are 12 inches by 24 inches. We might say that the area is 288 square inches or, if we used feet as our unit of measurement, we might say that the area is 2 square feet. If we were in a country using the metric system of measurement, we would determine the length and width to be approximately 60 centimeters and 30 centimeters, and we would say that the area is 1,800 square centimeters.

From this perspective, there is not a functional relationship between an object and the number used to denote its area, unless you specify the unit measurement. So we need to look at the numbers and what the numbers mean. For example, suppose you have heard that the floor space of the student center is 10,000 square feet. What does that number mean? Write your thoughts and then share them with your partners.

3.   Now let us examine a problem to explore the meaning of numbers in measurement. Mikala has a problem:

> The area of her lawn is 1,200 square feet. She wants to spread fertilizer over the lawn, but the bag of fertilizer says that one bag will cover 100 square yards. How many bags of fertilizer should she buy?

   a. Think about this problem—what you know about feet and yards, and the tools you have for problem-solving (such as Polya's 4 steps). Write down your initial thoughts and hypotheses, including an estimate if you feel you can make one.

   b. Meet with your partner(s). Select one or more ideas to pursue and then pursue them.

4.   After the class discussion, write your second draft response to the question asked in step 1. When you see a measurement (for example, 20,000 square feet), what does that number mean?

EXPLORATION 10.7   **Exploring Area on Geoboards**

Let us explore the concept of area and some area formulas using geoboards.

PART 1: Area on the geoboard

In our explorations on the geoboard and on dot paper, we will discuss the areas of figures in reference to the unit square—that is, the area enclosed by the smallest square you can make on your geoboard.

1.   **a.** Make as many "different" squares as you can on the geoboard or dot paper supplied at the end of the book.

   b. Compare your results and your strategies with your partner(s).

c. Determine the area of each of the squares.

d. Challenge: Can you make a square with an area of 1 unit? 2 units? 3 units, and so on? Which squares can't be made? Can you explain why they are impossible?

2. **a.** Make as many "different" rectangles as you can on the geoboard or dot paper provided by your instructor.

b. Compare your results and your strategies with your partner(s).

c. Determine the area of each of the rectangles.

d. Challenge: Can you make a rectangle with an area of 1 unit? 2 units? 3 units, and so on? Which rectangles can't be made? Can you explain why they are impossible?

3. **a.** Determine the area enclosed by each of the figures on page 269. Briefly describe your solution path so that a reader could see how you determined the area.

b. Compare your answers and your strategies with your partner(s).

c. With your partner, make an unusual shape on the geoboard. Determine the area independently, and then compare answers and solution strategies. Do this for several figures.

d. Summarize and justify useful strategies that you developed. Imagine writing this and sending it to a friend in order to spare your friend your struggles with these figures.

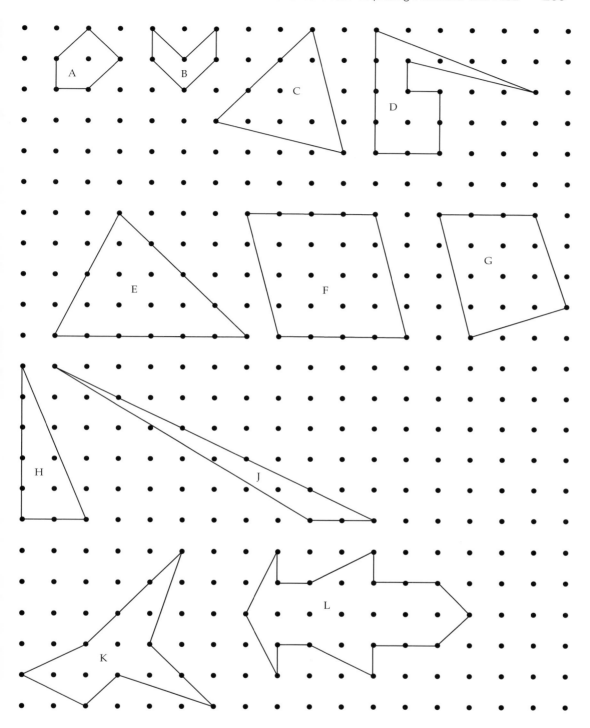

PART 2: Understanding area formulas

1.   *Determining the area of parallelograms.* Let us now explore certain other geometric figures and try to understand why their area formulas work. Even if you already remember certain area formulas (from previous experience), the purpose of these explorations is not to get the formula, but to understand why it works. The *why*

enables us to apply our understanding to new situations. For example, if you really understand why the formulas for the area of a rectangle, a parallelogram, and a triangle work, then you can use that knowledge to construct the formula for the area of a trapezoid. In that spirit, examine the parallelograms below.

a. Determine the area of the parallelograms below by a means other than using a formula. Can you see any patterns that are true for all four parallelograms? (Make more parallelograms if you wish.)

b. State and justify a formula for determining the area of any parallelogram.

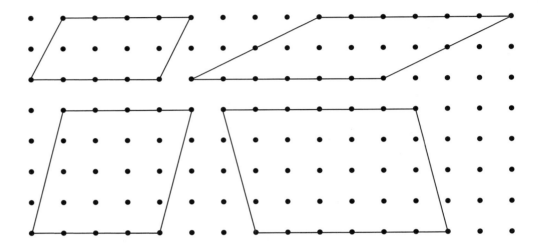

2. *Determining the area of triangles.* We can apply our understanding of the area of parallelograms to determine a way to find the area of any triangle.

a. Determine the area of the triangles below by a means other than using a formula. Can you discern any commonalities that enable us to determine the area of any triangle? (Make more triangles if you wish.)

b. State and justify a formula for determining the area of any triangle.

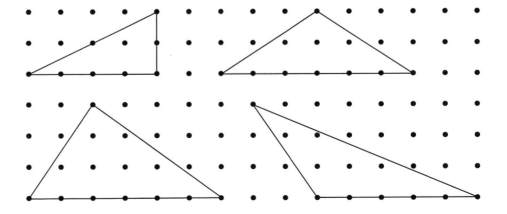

3. There is an old saying that "seeing is believing." Determine the areas of the triangles below—the right triangle, the obtuse triangle, and the isosceles triangle. What did you discover? Can you explain why what you discovered is true?

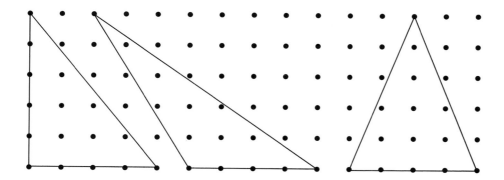

4. *Determining the area of trapezoids.*

   a. On your geoboard or dot paper (supplied at the end of the book), make several trapezoids, and determine the area of each trapezoid.

   b. Gather data on those attributes on which the area seems to depend. Can you see patterns in the numbers, and/or can you apply your work in the previous steps in this exploration so that you can draw a new trapezoid and predict the area based on certain measurements?

   c. After you are finished, write a chronological report. That is, tell the reader not only what you discovered but also how you discovered it. If you went down blind alleys or made and then discarded a hypothesis, help the reader to see why the blind alley or hypothesis made sense at the time and what you learned from that work.

EXPLORATION 10.8   **Exploring Relationships Between Perimeter and Area**

The relationship between perimeter and area is a rich field for exploration because there are many possible ways in which these two attributes can be related.

PART 1: Perimeters and areas on geoboards

1.   **a.** Suppose someone doubled the area of her garden. Does that mean that the length of the fence around the perimeter of her garden doubled also? What do you think?

b. If we know that the area of one garden is 50 percent greater than the area of another garden, does that mean that the perimeter will be 50 percent greater? What do you think?

c. Take some time to describe your present thoughts on the relationship between perimeter and area from this perspective.

The relationship between area and perimeter is not a simple one, and we are going to investigate the relationship systematically, using a technique developed by mathematicians that helps us when relationships are complicated. We are going to keep one variable constant and look at what happens to the other variable.

2.   **a.** On dot paper, make a number of polygons, each of which has an area of 15 units and in each of which all sides are either horizontal or vertical line segments. Determine the perimeter of each figure. In this case, we are holding area and certain attributes of shape constant and looking at how the perimeter changes.

b. Look at those figures with the smallest perimeters and those with the greatest perimeters. Describe differences between the figures with smaller perimeters and the figures with greater perimeters.

3.   **a.** Now make a number of polygons, each of which has a perimeter of 24 units and in each of which all sides are either horizontal or vertical line segments. Determine the area of each figure. In this case, we are holding perimeter and certain attributes of shape constant and looking at how the area changes.

b. Look at those figures that have the smallest areas and those figures that have the largest areas. Describe differences between the figures with smaller areas and the figures with larger areas.

4. Now, consider the original question: How are perimeter and area related? What do you believe now? Describe your present beliefs. If they are different from or more refined than your previous beliefs, describe the experiences, observations, or conversations that changed your beliefs.

PART 2: Changing dimensions

Let us explore the relationship between perimeter and area from another perspective.

1. What if you doubled the length of a rectangle but didn't change the width? The area would double, but what about the perimeter? What would be the effect on the perimeter? Explore this question with rectangles of different dimensions. Can you arrive at a statement that will be true for *all* rectangles? Write a report containing the following material:

   a. A brief summary of what you did.

   b. Your present description, in words and/or a formula, of the relationship between the original and the new perimeter.

2. Exchange descriptions with a partner. Provide feedback with respect to accuracy and clarity.

Looking Back on Exploration 10.8

What did you learn from this exploration?

EXPLORATION 10.9   What Does π Mean?

1. What does π mean? Suppose someone asked you this question. The person knows that the value of π is approximately 3.14, but does not have a sense of what π means. How would you answer that question? Write your first draft thoughts before reading on.

2. After observing your instructor's demonstration or doing explorations provided by instructor, describe what π means (second draft).

3. In groups of three, go through the following process:

   a. Each person reads their response. The others give feedback with respect to the accuracy and clarity of the response, in that order.

      - Accuracy: If a group member feels that the statement is not entirely accurate, discuss this issue until it is resolved.
      - Clarity: If a group member feels that certain words or phrases are ambiguous or unclear or vague, discuss those issues until they are resolved.

   b. Write down your third draft of "what π means."

Looking Back on Exploration 10.9

1.   State and then describe something important that you learned from this exploration.

2.   State and explain any questions you have about π at this point.

EXPLORATION 10.10   **Exploring the Area of a Circle**

The purpose of this exploration is to develop an understanding of the formula for the area of a circle.

1.   Cut the circle (at the end of this book) into sectors as shown below. Arrange these sectors into a "parallelogram," as shown.

 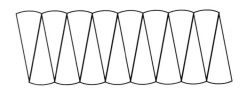

2.   If the radius of the circle is *r*, determine the length and width of the parallelogram in terms of *r*.

3.   Use this information to determine the area of the circle. Explain both the *what* and the *why* of your work.

Looking Back on Exploration 10.10

1.   State and then describe something important that you learned from this exploration.

2.   State and explain any questions you have about π or circles at this point.

EXPLORATION 10.11   **Can You Make the Quilt Pattern?**

In Chapter 9 we explored quilt structures and symmetries. In this chapter, we will explore a problem that real quilters face: making actual quilt blocks. This problem requires us to apply our understanding of measurement ideas.

PART 1: Variations

Below are two variations of a star pattern.

1.   Describe how the two patterns are alike and different.

2.   Make a copy of each pattern. Include the measurements of the sides of each figure.

PART 2: Similar patterns

Examine the Cats and Mice pattern and the Eight Hands Round pattern.

1.   How are they similar and how are they different?

2.   Describe figures in the two patterns that are mathematically similar.

Cats And Mice   Eight Hands Round

PART 3: Challenges

Each of the following quilt blocks presents different challenges. For each block that you make:

1. Explain any quilt structures (such as patches, an 8-point star, or a hexagon).

2. Justify your choice of dimensions for the whole block (not all are squares).

3. Give step-by-step directions for making the figure. Include the length of each segment and degrees (when appropriate).

4. Describe your biggest challenge and how you overcame it.

5. Describe any insights, observations, what ifs, or questions that you have.

Arabic Lattice

Card Tricks

Cobweb

Grandmother's Fan[1]

Hope of Hartford[1]

[1] From Luanne Seymour Cohen, *Quilt Design Masters* (Palo Alto, Calif.: Dale Seymour Publications, 1996).

Irish Puzzle

Puss in the Corner

The Reel

Star 1

Star 2

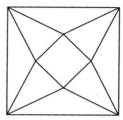

World Without End

PART 4: Quilting and systems of measurement

When quilting was invented, quilters used the English system of measurement. Because of this, many of the computations are cumbersome. Suppose you heard of a new quilting book with lots of great designs in which all the measurements were metric. Describe the pros and cons of switching to metric quilting.

EXPLORATION 10.12   **How Much Will the Carpet Cost?**

I have seen problems like the following in many, many textbooks:

> Betty and Bruce have decided that the old carpeting in their living room has to go. They saw an advertisement on television for carpeting at $15.95 per square yard. Their living room measures 25 feet by 18 feet. How much will the new carpet cost?

The correct "mathematical" answer is obtained by the following process:

1. Find the area of the room: $25 \cdot 18 = 450$ square feet.
2. Convert from square feet to square yards: 450 square feet ÷ 9 square feet/square yard = 50 square yards.
3. Multiply this area by $15.95: (50 square yards)($15.95/square yard) = $795.50.

There is a major problem with this process: This is not at all how the carpet store determines how much your carpet will cost.

1. Brainstorm how the carpet store might determine the cost. Imagine that you are the manager of the store and/or that you are the person who installs the carpet. Summarize the results of your brainstorming as statements and/or questions.

2. After the class discussion, summarize the relevant information you will use to determine the cost of the carpet.

3. Now determine how much the carpet store would actually charge Betty and Bruce.

4. Determine the cost of carpet for each of the rooms below.

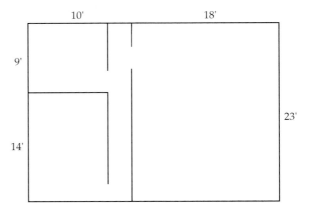

Looking Back on Exploration 10.12

1. State and then describe something important that you learned from this exploration.

2. State and explain any questions you have about carpeting at this point.

E X P L O R A T I O N 10.13   **Irregular Areas**

Outside the classroom, when we want to find an area, more often than not the object is not one for which we have a nice, simple formula. However, we can use our knowledge of area to determine the areas of these objects. Applying your understanding of what area means, determine which of the two ponds below is bigger.

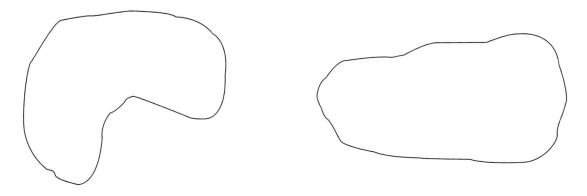

1. Brainstorm different ways to determine which of these two ponds is bigger (feel free to use your imagination). Briefly summarize the methods that arose in your group.

2. **a.** During the class discussion, make notes of the pros and cons of each method, using a table like the one below. If you think any of the methods are not valid or will not be reasonably accurate, describe those concerns in your "cons."

	Pros	Cons
Method 1		
Method 2		
etc.		

b. Note any other important statements or points made in the class discussion.

3. Select two methods that could be used to determine the actual area and determine the area of each of the ponds using that method. For each method:

a. Describe your work.

b. Justify the precision in your answer — that is, the choice of units, and the number of decimal places, if any.

c. Describe any difficulties you had and how you overcame them.

d. Describe any changes or modifications in your ideas with respect to the methods discussed in the previous step.

Looking Back on Exploration 10.13

1. State and then describe something important that you learned from this exploration.

2. State and explain any questions you have about measuring the areas of irregularly shaped objects at this point.

EXPLORATION 10.14   **Functions, Geometric Figures, and Geoboards**

Throughout this book, we have seen that there are many functional relationships in mathematics and in everyday life. In this exploration, we will discover relationships among three variables: the area of a figure, the number of pegs on the border of the figure, and the number of pegs in the interior of the figure.

PART 1: Exploring the relationships between pegs and triangles

1. Use your geoboards or dot paper (supplied at the back of the book) to fill in a table like the one below. When a member of the group notices a pattern, discuss and note that pattern. Does that pattern lead to a hypothesis? For example, can you predict the area or number of border pegs or interior pegs in the next triangle?

2.   When you feel that you are able to predict the area and the number of border and interior pegs given only the dimensions of the triangle, state your hypothesis and how you came to discover it.

Dimension of the right triangle	Area	Number of border pegs	Number of interior pegs	Insights/observations
3 by 3	4.5 sq. units	9	1	
4 by 3				
5 by 3				
6 by 3				
7 by 3				
8 by 3				
9 by 3				
10 by 3				
11 by 3				

3.   Predict the values for the three columns in a 16 by 3 triangle and a 20 by 3 rectangle. Explain your predictions.

4.   **a.**   Make a graph to show the relationship between the length of the longer leg and the area of the triangle.

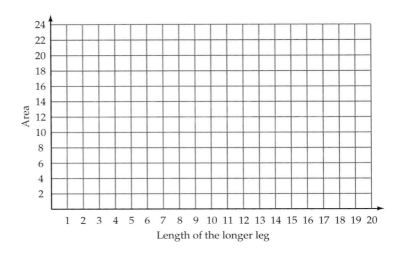

b. What does this graph's being a straight line mean?

5. In this step you are going to graph two different relationships on the same graph.

a. First plot the points representing the relationship between the length of the longer leg and the number of border pegs. Then plot the points representing the relationship between the length of the longer leg and the number of interior pegs.

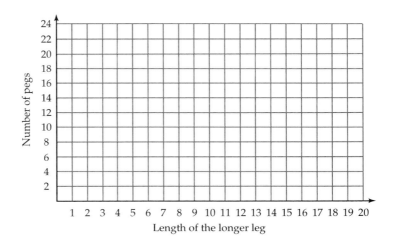

b. What does neither of these graph's being a straight line mean? Justify your response.

c. Does it mean that they are not functions? Justify your response.

d. Describe patterns that you see in these two graphs.

e. Can you make use of these patterns to extend the graphs—that is, to predict the number of interior and border pegs when the length of the longer base is 12, 13, 14, 15, or more units long?

f. State your hypothesis now for predicting the number of interior and border pegs for any right triangle. Justify your hypothesis.

PART 2: Expanding our exploration to other figures

We are going to expand our exploration of relationships among border and interior pegs to include other figures. We are also going to change the focus slightly. Now, we are going to look for patterns so that we can predict the area of any geometric figure on the geoboard from the number of border and interior pegs.

1. Make several geometric figures on your geoboard or dot paper. In each case, determine the area (A), the number of border pegs (B), and the number of interior pegs (I). Do you notice any patterns that lead to hypotheses? If you do, record your hypothesis and how it came to be. Test your hypothesis. If it works, great. If not, back to the drawing board. If you do not see patterns that lead to hypotheses, move on to another geometric figure.

Geometric figure	Area (A)	Number of border pegs (B)	Number of interior pegs (I)

2. Now that you have determined the relationship between the three variables B, I, and A, look back and describe the moment of discovery.

SECTION 10.3 **EXPLORING SURFACE AREA AND VOLUME**

Many applications of measurement involve three-dimensional surfaces—either covering them (surface area) or filling them (volume).

EXPLORATION 10.15 **Understanding Surface Area**

1. How would you determine the surface areas of each of the objects below? Write down your thoughts.

    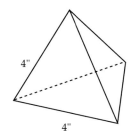

2. Meet with your partners and pool your ideas. Write down those ideas that the whole group understands and agrees with. The purpose of this step is not for someone who knows the formula to explain it to others so that they can copy it down. The purpose of this step is to discuss ideas and then note those ideas that make sense to the whole group.

3. Each person in the group will now construct a net [see Exploration 8.12 (Understanding Solids), Part 3] to make one of the models above. Remember that a net is a connected two-dimensional figure that can be folded up to make a polyhedron. Test each net by folding it to make the solid shape.

4. Each person presents and describes a net to the rest of the group.

5. Now describe how to find the surface area of each of the figures.

6. **a.** Describe the commonalities and differences among the first three figures.

Commonalities	Differences

Commonalities	Differences

b. Describe a general formula for determining the surface area of any *prism*.

Looking Back on Exploration 10.15

1. State and then describe something important that you learned from this exploration.

2. State and explain any questions you have about surface area.

EXPLORATION 10.16 Understanding Volume

PART 1: Volume of a cube

1. You probably know the formula for determining the volume of a rectangular prism: length · width · height. Can you justify this formula—that is, can you explain why we multiply these three numbers? Write your first draft ideas.

2. Your instructor will give you a rectangular prism to fill with cubes. Do so and then revisit your response to the previous question. If you wish to revise it, do so now, and also explain what happened that led you to decide to revise your answer.

3. A manufacturer sells widgets. Each widget is put in a box whose dimensions are 4 cm × 6 cm × 10 cm. The shipping box is 80 cm × 60 cm × 40 cm. If the company makes 100,000 widgets each year, how many shipping boxes does it need?

    a. Using your knowledge of volume and your problem-solving tools, begin to work on this problem.

    b. Discuss your ideas with your partner(s). Remember to treat ideas as hypotheses: They may or may not be valid. Therefore, the purpose of the group conversation is to convince yourselves of the validity or nonvalidity of hypotheses that are raised.

    c. Describe your solution path and answer.

4. Let's say the company also manufactures gizmos. Suppose the dimensions of the box containing a gizmo are 3.5 cm × 7.6 cm × 11.3 cm, and your shipping box is 80 cm × 60 cm × 40 cm. How should the company arrange the gizmo boxes so that each shipping box will contain the maximum possible number of gizmos?

    a. Using your knowledge of volume and your problem-solving tools, begin to work on this problem.

    b. Discuss your ideas with your partner(s), remembering to treat ideas as hypotheses [as in Step 3(b)].

    c. Describe your solution path and answer.

5. Let's say each object is placed in a box whose dimensions are a, b, and c, and the dimensions of the shipping box are x, y, and z. Under what conditions will the following formula work for determining the number of small boxes that one shipping box will contain:

$$\text{Number of objects} = \frac{xyz}{abc}$$

    a. Using your knowledge of volume and your problem-solving tools, begin to work on this problem.

    b. Discuss your ideas with your partner(s), treating ideas as hypotheses.

    c. Describe your solution path and answer.

6. The United States Postal Service sells boxes. At the time of the writing of this book, these were the dimensions and prices of the boxes:

8″ × 8″ × 8″	$1.00
16″ × 12″ × 4″	$1.25
17″ × 11″ × 10″	$1.30
20″ × 14″ × 10″	$1.75
Tube 3″ diameter by $18\frac{1}{4}$″ length	$1.00
Tube 3″ diameter by 30″ length	$1.50

a. Are the prices of the boxes proportional to the volumes? Use your knowledge of volume and proportion and your problem-solving tools to work on this problem. State and justify your answer.

b. Are the prices proportional to the surface areas? State and justify your answer.

c. Which do you think is the more important measure in determining the cost of the boxes — surface area or volume? Justify your response.

PART 2: Volume of a cylinder

1. By now you should be comfortable with the formula for the area of a rectangular prism. What about the volume of a cylinder? Since its base is not a rectangle, we cannot determine its volume by filling it with little cubes. We must use reasoning to develop and then test our conjectures with respect to what its volume might be. Look back at the cylinder that you made from a net in Exploration 10.15. Describe your present thoughts concerning how to find the volume of that cylinder. Justify your reasoning.

2. There are several activities that you can do to justify and better understand how to find the volume of a cylinder. Below are several possibilities that will serve as hints. Explore one or more of these hints, and then summarize what you did and what you learned from the exploration.

a. Look at the commonalities among the surface areas of prisms. Imagine making prisms in which the base has more and more sides.

b. Mark lines on your cylinder at 1 inch high, 2 inches high, and so on. Imagine slicing the cylinder at these points, so that your cylinder consists of 4 of these slices.

c. Get a stick of modeling clay and make two congruent rectangular prisms that are 4 inches by 4 inches by 1 inch in height. Take one of those prisms and remold it so that you have a cylinder that is 1 inch tall. Obviously you have the same volumes. What does this suggest about how to find the volume of a cylinder?

3. State the formula for finding the volume of a cylinder and provide your justification of this formula in your own words.

PART 3: Volume of a pyramid

1. Look back at the models of a cube and a pyramid that you made from nets in Exploration 10.15. Describe your current thoughts concerning how to find the volume of that pyramid. It is important to note that "your current thoughts" is not the same as "your guess as to the formula." Rather, it is your thoughts about how we might find the volume of a pyramid. Your thoughts may contain some quantitative thinking—for example, recall Investigation 10.4, concerning the area of a circle, where we found that the area of a circle must be less than $4r^2$.

2. If you look closely at the pyramid and the cube, you will find some commonalities. If you haven't noticed them yet, examine these figures and discuss them now in the group and discuss how they might provide more clues about the connections between determining the volume of a cube and a pyramid. Write down your thoughts.

3. Your instructor will provide you with some material. Fill your pyramid and see how much bigger the volume of the cube is than that of the pyramid. Before doing so, state your guess and any reasoning. Then do so.

4. Describe your present thinking about the relationship between the size of a cube and the size of a pyramid. State your thinking as carefully as possible. For example, it would not be accurate to say that the area of a cube is bigger than the area of a pyramid; to be accurate, this statement would need to indicate the conditions under which this would be true.

Looking Back on Exploration 10.16

1. State and then describe something important that you learned from this exploration.

2. State and explain any questions you have about volume at this point.

EXPLORATION 10.17   **Applying Volume Concepts**

Let's say you started a company that manufactures a healthy, natural cereal. The dimensions of your cereal boxes are 24 cm by 16 cm by 5 cm. However, many customers have asked that you make a bigger box. Design a box that is similar in shape that will hold exactly 3 times as much cereal.

Your report of your findings needs to include:

1. Your actual work (not to be graded; may be messy).

2. Your answer.

3. Your degree of confidence about your answer and a brief explanation of your confidence; if your degree of confidence is not very high, state your uncertainty as questions.

4. A narrative description of how you arrived at your answer. This description may be a "tour" through your work.

5. A description of the biggest problem you encountered and how you overcame it.

EXPLORATION 10.18   **Determining Volumes of Irregularly Shaped Objects**

PART 1: Getting started and making predictions

1. **a.** When you go to the store, which size egg do you buy: medium, large, extra large, or jumbo? Why?

  b. Why don't we call the smallest size egg *small* instead of *medium*?

2. Are you getting the same value for your money with different-sized eggs? That is, would an egg that is twice as big cost twice as much? Write down your initial thoughts.

3. In mathematical terms, what would it mean to say that you are getting the same value when you buy a medium egg as when you buy a jumbo egg?

4. Do you think each of the sizes will be about the same value, or do you think they will vary (remember the 8-inch and 16-inch pizzas from Investigation 10.5)? Explain your reasoning. If you think the value will vary, predict the rank in terms of best value first, and explain your reasoning.

PART 2: Volume and cost

1. **a.** If we took 100 eggs of the same size and found their volume, predict the variation you would expect. For example, what would be the ratio of the volumes of the largest and smallest eggs? Explain your prediction.

   b. If you were to graph the data with the volume as the independent variable and the frequency of each size as the dependent variable, do you think the graph would be uniform, normal, bimodal, or random? Explain your prediction.

2. Determine the volumes of the eggs and then determine the average volume for each size egg.

3. Determine the relative value for each size. That is, are you getting approximately the same value for your money in each case?

PART 3: Mass and cost

1. **a.** If we took 100 eggs of the same size and found their mass, predict the variation you would expect. For example, what would be the ratio of the masses of the largest and smallest eggs? Explain your prediction.

   b. If you were to graph the data with the mass as the independent variable and the frequency of each size as the dependent variable, do you think the graph would be uniform, normal, bimodal, or random? Explain your prediction.

2. Determine the masses of the eggs and then determine the average mass for each size egg.

3. Determine the relative value for each size. That is, are you getting approximately the same value for your money in each case?

PART 4: Mass and volume

1. Do you think the masses and volumes of different eggs will be proportional? First, explain in your own words what the question means. Then write down your hypothesis and explain your reasoning.

2. Using the data from Parts 2 and 3, determine the answer to the question from your data.

Extension question: How do you think eggs are actually sized: mass, volume, length, width, or something else?

Looking Back on Exploration 10.18

1. State and then describe something important that you learned from this exploration.

2. State and explain any questions you have about this exploration.

EXPLORATION 10.19 **Paper Towels**

PART 1: Initial questions and ideas

Most households in the United States use paper towels. Putting aside for the moment the issues of conservation and waste, let's say you were in a supermarket and you were deciding which paper towel to buy.

1. What are some of the factors that might enter into one's decision to buy a particular brand of paper towel?

2. How would you determine which brand of towel is the "cheapest"?

PART 2: Absorbency

1. Let's say you were more interested in absorbency than in anything else. That is, you want the towel that will absorb the most liquid. How might you detemine the most absorbent towel? Write down your initial ideas. After discussing ideas with your partner(s), develop a plan and then determine the most absorbent towel.

2.   Your report must contain:

    a.   Your plan and a justification of each step.

    b.   Your actual data and conclusion. The reader must be able to see what you did and how you arrived at your conclusion.

    c.   Your justification of the precision in your answer — for example, the choice of unit and the number of decimal places, if any.

    d.   A description and explanation of your degree of confidence in your result.

    e.   A description of any difficulties you had and how you overcame them, either totally or partially.

3.   Present your findings to the class. After the class presentations, describe and explain any changes you would make in your design.

PART 3: Strength

1.   Let's say that you were more interested in strength: You want a towel that won't shred when you clean surfaces with it. How might you determine the strongest paper towel? Write down your initial ideas. After discussing ideas with your partners, develop a plan and then determine the strongest towel.

2.   Your report must contain:

    a.   Your plan and a justification of each step.

    b.   Your actual data and conclusion. The reader must be able to see what you did and how you arrived at your conclusion.

    c.   Your justification of the precision in your answer — for example, the choice of unit and the number of decimal places, if any.

    d.   A description and explanation of your degree of confidence in your result.

e. A description of any difficulties you had and how you overcome them, either totally or partially.

3. Present your findings to the class. After the class presentations, describe and explain any changes you would make in your design.

Looking Back on Exploration 10.19

State and then describe something important that you learned from this investigation.

EXPLORATION 10.20 **Measurement, Ambiguity, and Precision**

Most textbook problems are well defined, but many, if not most, real-life problems are not well defined. Below are five problems that are not well defined. In some cases, you need to gather more information in order to solve the problem. In all cases, you need to make (and justify) assumptions in order to solve the problem.

Each group will select a question, determine a solution, and present the group solution to the class.

Your report of your findings needs to include:

a. Your solution in a two-column format:

- The left column contains the actual mathematical computations.

- The right column describes the assumptions you made in order to solve the problem and justifies/explains why you are doing what you are doing.

b. Your degree of confidence about your answer and a brief explanation of your confidence; if your degree of confidence is not very high, state your uncertainty as questions.

c. A description and justification of the assumptions you made in order to solve this problem.

d. A description of the biggest mathematical problem you encountered along the way and how you overcame it.

e. A description of your one or two most important learnings about mathematics and/or about problem solving.

Questions:
1. McDonalds has now sold over 100 billion hamburgers. Tell us about how much 100 billion hamburgers is. At least one aspect should be to describe how much

volume this many hamburgers would take up; you may, but are not required to, represent this answer as a cube.

2. It is estimated that approximately 16 billion disposable diapers are sold each year in the United States. How much volume does this amount of diapers represent?

3. Myra believes that it would be cheaper to make soda cans in the shape of prisms (like children's juice boxes) rather than the present cylinders. Do you agree or disagree with this premise? Describe the pros and cons, both mathematical and other, of making soda cans in the shape of prisms.

4. I once heard on the radio that Congress had just appropriated money to increase office space by 65,000 square feet and to add 18,000 square feet of parking. How many parking spaces can be gotten from 18,000 square feet? Draw a rough blueprint for the parking lot—total dimensions, length and width of parking spaces, the width of the "lanes," and so on.

5. One of the things I miss most about high school teaching is that in high school I had my own room and could decorate it as I wished. College teachers do not have their own classrooms, and so the walls of most college classrooms are rather bare. One day I thought that if we could cover the walls of each college classroom with corkboard, it would make posting things on the wall easier. I wondered how much this would cost. How much would it cost to cover the walls of your present classroom with corkboard?

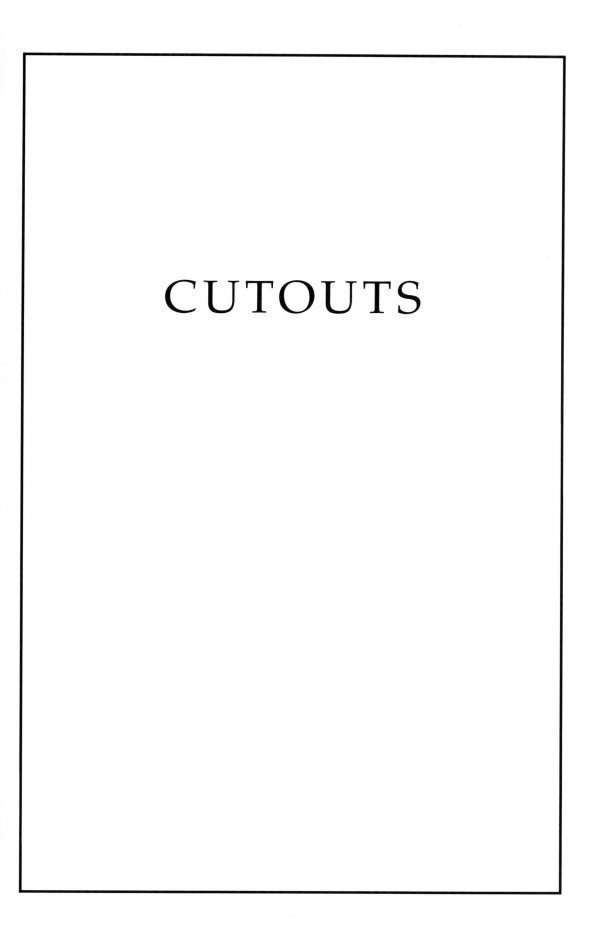

CUTOUTS

Longs, Flats, and Units

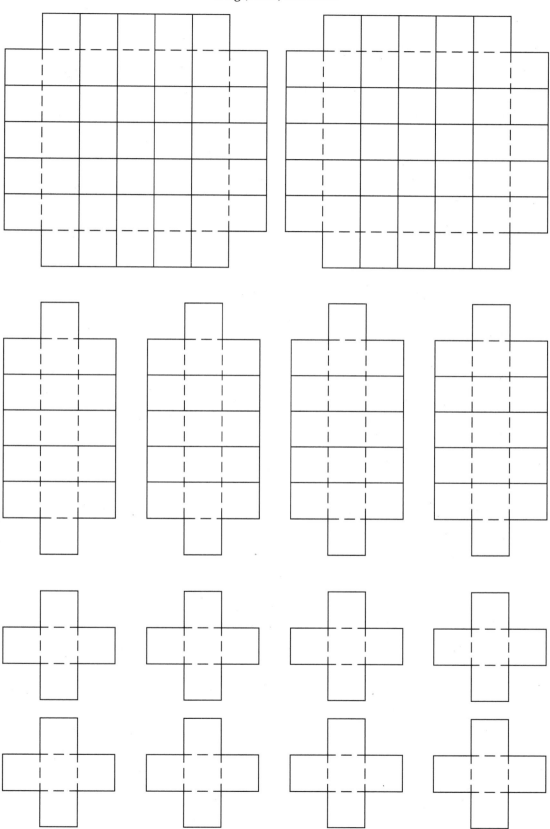

Patterns in Multiples

Multiples of 2

0	1	2	3	4	5	6	7	8	9
10	11	12	13	14	15	16	17	18	19
20	21	22	23	24	25	26	27	28	29
30	31	32	33	34	35	36	37	38	39
40	41	42	43	44	45	46	47	48	49
50	51	52	53	54	55	56	57	58	59
60	61	62	63	64	65	66	67	68	69
70	71	72	73	74	75	76	77	78	79
80	81	82	83	84	85	86	87	88	89
90	91	92	93	94	95	96	97	98	99

Multiples of 3

0	1	2	3	4	5	6	7	8	9
10	11	12	13	14	15	16	17	18	19
20	21	22	23	24	25	26	27	28	29
30	31	32	33	34	35	36	37	38	39
40	41	42	43	44	45	46	47	48	49
50	51	52	53	54	55	56	57	58	59
60	61	62	63	64	65	66	67	68	69
70	71	72	73	74	75	76	77	78	79
80	81	82	83	84	85	86	87	88	89
90	91	92	93	94	95	96	97	98	99

Multiples of 4

0	1	2	3	4	5	6	7	8	9
10	11	12	13	14	15	16	17	18	19
20	21	22	23	24	25	26	27	28	29
30	31	32	33	34	35	36	37	38	39
40	41	42	43	44	45	46	47	48	49
50	51	52	53	54	55	56	57	58	59
60	61	62	63	64	65	66	67	68	69
70	71	72	73	74	75	76	77	78	79
80	81	82	83	84	85	86	87	88	89
90	91	92	93	94	95	96	97	98	99

Multiples of 5

0	1	2	3	4	5	6	7	8	9
10	11	12	13	14	15	16	17	18	19
20	21	22	23	24	25	26	27	28	29
30	31	32	33	34	35	36	37	38	39
40	41	42	43	44	45	46	47	48	49
50	51	52	53	54	55	56	57	58	59
60	61	62	63	64	65	66	67	68	69
70	71	72	73	74	75	76	77	78	79
80	81	82	83	84	85	86	87	88	89
90	91	92	93	94	95	96	97	98	99

Multiples of 6

0	1	2	3	4	5	6	7	8	9
10	11	12	13	14	15	16	17	18	19
20	21	22	23	24	25	26	27	28	29
30	31	32	33	34	35	36	37	38	39
40	41	42	43	44	45	46	47	48	49
50	51	52	53	54	55	56	57	58	59
60	61	62	63	64	65	66	67	68	69
70	71	72	73	74	75	76	77	78	79
80	81	82	83	84	85	86	87	88	89
90	91	92	93	94	95	96	97	98	99

Multiples of 7

0	1	2	3	4	5	6	7	8	9
10	11	12	13	14	15	16	17	18	19
20	21	22	23	24	25	26	27	28	29
30	31	32	33	34	35	36	37	38	39
40	41	42	43	44	45	46	47	48	49
50	51	52	53	54	55	56	57	58	59
60	61	62	63	64	65	66	67	68	69
70	71	72	73	74	75	76	77	78	79
80	81	82	83	84	85	86	87	88	89
90	91	92	93	94	95	96	97	98	99

Multiples of 8

0	1	2	3	4	5	6	7	8	9
10	11	12	13	14	15	16	17	18	19
20	21	22	23	24	25	26	27	28	29
30	31	32	33	34	35	36	37	38	39
40	41	42	43	44	45	46	47	48	49
50	51	52	53	54	55	56	57	58	59
60	61	62	63	64	65	66	67	68	69
70	71	72	73	74	75	76	77	78	79
80	81	82	83	84	85	86	87	88	89
90	91	92	93	94	95	96	97	98	99

Multiples of 9

0	1	2	3	4	5	6	7	8	9
10	11	12	13	14	15	16	17	18	19
20	21	22	23	24	25	26	27	28	29
30	31	32	33	34	35	36	37	38	39
40	41	42	43	44	45	46	47	48	49
50	51	52	53	54	55	56	57	58	59
60	61	62	63	64	65	66	67	68	69
70	71	72	73	74	75	76	77	78	79
80	81	82	83	84	85	86	87	88	89
90	91	92	93	94	95	96	97	98	99

Base 10 Circle Clocks

Counting by 1

Counting by 2

Counting by 3

Counting by 4

Counting by 5

Counting by 6

Counting by 7

Counting by 8

Counting by 9

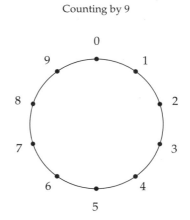

Base 10 Graph Paper

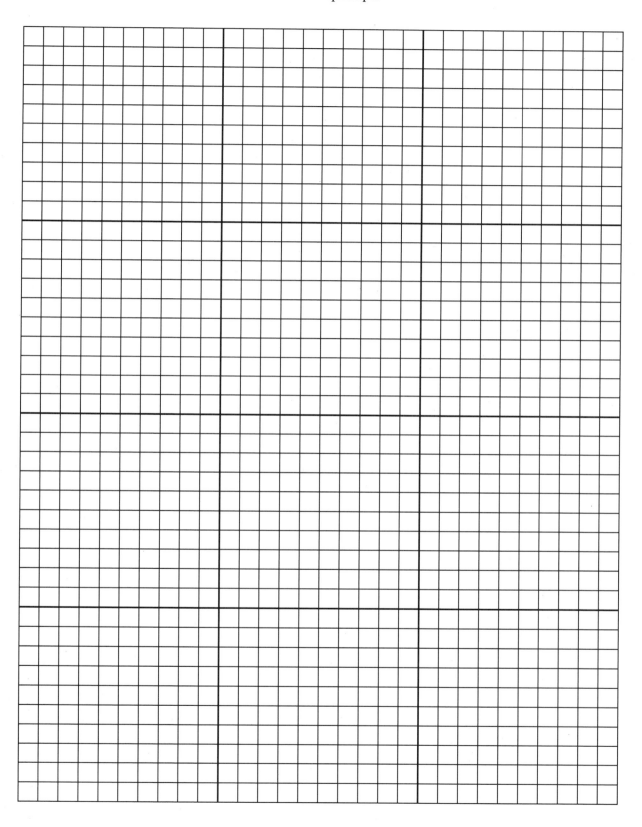

Other Base Graph Paper

Map of the United States

ME
NH
VT
MA
RI
CT
NY
NJ
DE
MD
PA
WV
VA
NC
SC
FL
OH
KY
TN
GA
AL
MI
IN
IL
MS
WI
MO
AR
LA
IA
MN
OK
KS
TX
ND
SD
NE
CO
NM
HI
MT
WY
UT
AR
ID
NV
CA
WA
OR
AK

Geoboards

Regular Polygons

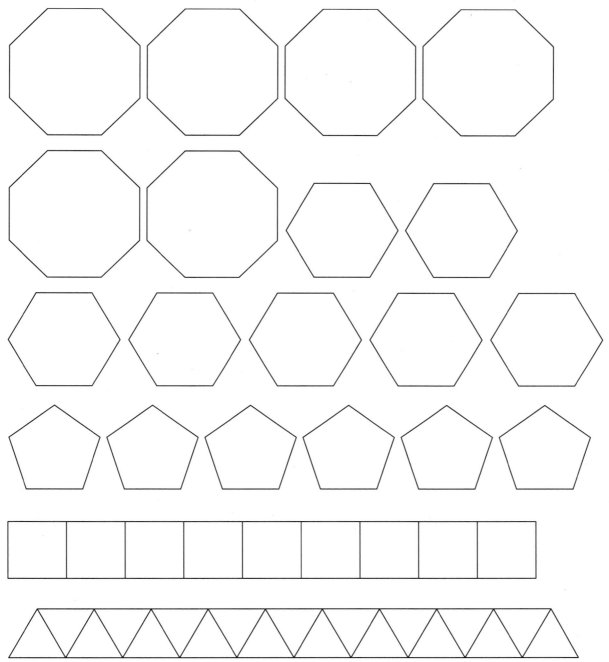

Exploring the Area of a Circle

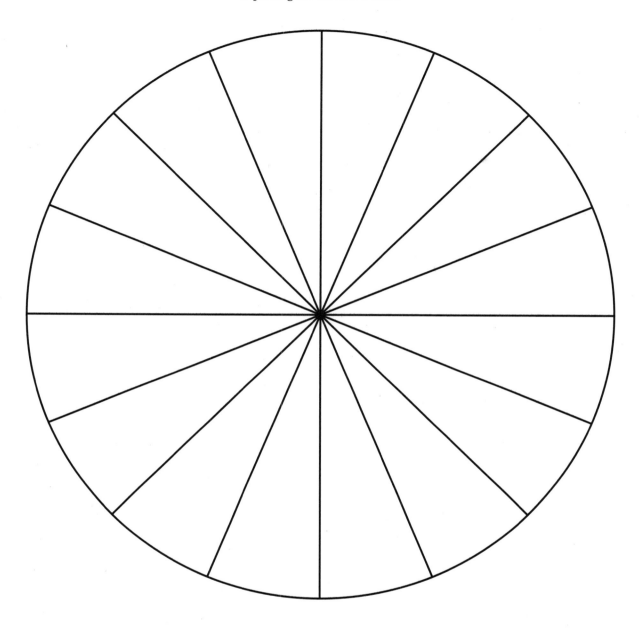